A GUIDE TO OPERATIONAL
RESEARCH

A Guide to
Operational Research

W. E. DUCKWORTH

Fellow of the Institute of Statisticians
Fellow of the Institution of Metallurgists

METHUEN & CO LTD
11 New Fetter Lane London EC4

First published 1962
Second edition 1965
Reprinted twice
SBN 416 40780 3

First published as a University Paperback 1965
Reprinted five times
Reprinted 1972
SBN 416 68700 8

Printed in Great Britain by photo-litho
by T. & A. Constable Limited, Edinburgh

Distributed in the USA by
HARPER & ROW, PUBLISHERS INC.
BARNES & NOBLE IMPORT DIVISION

CONTENTS

PREFACE

There is nothing more difficult to take in hand, more perilous to conduct, or more uncertain in its success, than to take the lead in the introduction of a new order of things, because the innovator has for enemies all those who have done well under the old conditions, and lukewarm defenders in those who may do well under the new.

MACHIAVELLI: *The Prince*

Arthur Mee's admirable guide-books to the English Counties used to carry on the flysheet the somewhat two-edged assertion, 'There have been many books on Blankshire, but never one like this'. If you substitute Operational Research for Blankshire you will have the author's intention about this book.

My aim is, above all, to produce a book which is readable. The message of Operational Research which I hope to expound is a message directed at managers. Such men have little enough time to read the masses of company documents and statistics which modern administration proliferates in such expanding volume. To expect them to turn with eagerness at the fag-end of a long day to an esoteric treatise on matrix algebra or the theory of convex sets is to expect a level of superhumanity which, if it were realizable in our managers, would not need the assistance of Operational Research.

The book therefore contains the very minimum of mathematics and such as there is can be skipped without loss of understanding of principles. The philosophy and techniques of Operational Research will be presented mainly in a discursive way, as in a chat between friends, and if my professional colleagues argue, as no doubt they will in such reviews as find their way into print, that a lot of precision is thereby lost, I refer them now to the much better books that have been written on the subject for those with the time to consume them.

Having talked about Operational Research for three paragraphs without defining it I had better get down to the job. Defining O.R., as it is conveniently abbreviated, has been as fascinating a pastime among O.R. workers as the ancient theological debates about angels on the points of pins. In this situation I feel rather like Mark Twain did about stopping smoking. 'It is the easiest thing in the world, I have done it hundreds of times.'

I shall define O.R. more comprehensively later, but I think that for the purpose of this preface and for drawing the interested reader further into the book, I would define it as the study of administrative systems pursued in the same scientific manner in which systems in physics, chemistry and biology are studied in the natural sciences.

The objective of the study is to gain understanding of these systems so that they may be more readily controlled, just as systems in the natural sciences are more readily controlled than they were and can in fact be harnessed to man's uses. Control, by the way, is used throughout this book in the regulative and not the restrictive sense.

We can now switch on an electric light with a good degree of probability that the bulb will light up. We can spray crops against certain diseases with a strong expectation that protection will be assured without the occurrence of unforeseen side effects. But can the average manager be as sure of the workings of his administrative system?

Can he say, 'I will reduce stocks to such and such a level and will not endanger my productive processes or let my customers down?' Can he say, 'I will change my distributive outlets and know that I shall be better off?' Can he in fact introduce any changes in routine and procedure without a considerable degree of uncertainty attending their results?

Does he know very often whether a change is necessary or even desirable? Modern industry is so very complex that the optimum point of operation of many of its systems is no longer within the intuitive comprehension of individuals.

To enable this intuition, this imaginative judgement, which is at the core of management to hold its rightful place in the controlling of such systems is the function of O.R. For its job is the study of these systems and the understanding of how they may be controlled by simple rules.

Managers often feel that scientific methods are a threat to their intuition, but I hope to show that the opposite is true.

In case you doubt the ability of simple rules to handle complex situations just consider, as Stafford Beer has pointed out, how the simple rule 'drive on the left' prevented chaos on the roads of Britain in the early days of motoring. The equally simple rule 'never turn across a stream of traffic in cities' might ease the traffic flow in our towns considerably. If, instead of holding up traffic as in the sketch below (Figure 1),

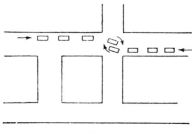

FIG. 1

drivers had to keep turning left until they could cross the traffic stream at right angles as in Figure 2,

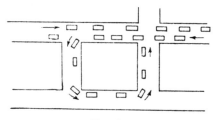

FIG. 2

then junctions controlled by traffic lights might handle a greater capacity of traffic than they do at present.

Because of the resistance to the scientific approach to management there is a need, I feel, for a book of this sort which puts the message and scope of the scientific approach across in the easily comprehensible form which is necessary not because managers have not the capacity to understand anything complicated (that is insulting and untrue), but because they have not got the time. This is an attempt, therefore, to explain O.R. and to give some account of its achievements in such a way that a man with three hours to spare and a good fire to sit by can digest it with his dinner.

It also aims to give sufficient guidance in certain cases to enable the reader to try a little 'do it yourself' O.R. where appropriate so that he may gain confidence in the techniques himself. In particular the Appendix on Statistical Methods is designed in this way so that the reader may familiarize himself, painlessly if possible, with the kind of thinking inherent in O.R.

To make the book a little more readable, footnotes have been eschewed. References are given, not by those irritating little numbers, thus [12], which one can never remember, but by the names of the authors in the reference quoted, thus: (Smith). This might not be remembered either, but at least it gives a more personal touch to acknowledgements to the work of others.

Finally, most of the techniques described will be illustrated by examples from the work of myself and my colleagues. This is not merely conceit, but is based upon a belief that first-hand knowledge is the best to relate and that, because my experience has been largely elementary, it will illustrate the principles more clearly.

Professor Homans, the American sociologist, wrote in *Nature* (December 1955):

'The practical value of any science is that by making experience subject to explicit intellectual control it speeds up the learning process and so sets intuition and judgement free to work on new ground rather than old. In something as important as management, anything that even begins to get us free of empiricism or to set empiricism free for new advances makes a contribution.'

This book, I hope, is such a contribution.

ACKNOWLEDGEMENTS

Some of the material used in this book has already appeared in *Engineering, Applied Statistics, Operational Research Quarterly, Metalworking Production, Metal Treatment, Data Processing, The Accountant* and *Metal Industry*. Permission to reproduce this material is gratefully acknowledged.

I wish to thank also Messrs P. P. Love, K. Seymour, F. D. Robinson, J. K. Wyatt and S. Babik for much helpful discussion and encouragement. Many other colleagues have given me inspiration and, where possible, they are acknowledged in the text.

Thanks are also due to Mrs B. Blinko, Mrs S. E. Cousens and Mrs P. M. Prance for doing so much of the typing in their spare time and to the Glacier Metal Co. for permission to reproduce so much material.

Some of the American material was provided by Mr R. R. Crane and his colleagues.

PART I:
WHAT OPERATIONAL RESEARCH IS

*When you can measure what you are speaking of and express it
in numbers you know that on which you are discoursing. But
when you cannot measure it and express it in numbers, your
knowledge is of a very meagre and unsatisfactory kind.*

LORD KELVIN

Introduction

This is a book about measurement in management. It is a book on how
Kelvin's dictum can be and should be applied in industrial management. Operational Research is concerned with the measurement of
industrial operations and because of this it is sometimes likened to
and confused with Work Study, Industrial Engineering, Management
Accountancy and other techniques which have been trumpeted into
the ears of line executives by their staff colleagues over the last decade.

Before attempting to distinguish between these management aids,
however, I would like to try and jump one hurdle which, unless it is
convincingly cleared both by myself and the reader will put a mental
blockage in the way of my message and of his understanding it. It is a
hurdle over which many aspirants to 'scientific' management may
stumble and thus it is as well to have it satisfactorily behind us.

I refer to the boundary between judgement and precision, between
discretion and measurement, between choice and control. Elliott
Jaques has pointed out that in industry men are paid for taking
decisions. Not for working long hours or controlling a lot of men or
running expensive machinery, but for exercising discretion, for making
choices between alternative courses of action and for making the
correct choices. This payment for using discretion, for employing

judgement and exercising imagination, is not always explicitly realized, as witness the arguments which take place over differential payments for train drivers and bus drivers, but it is implicitly realized and any encroachment into the discretion a person can exercise in his job is bitterly resented and feared.

It is precisely this encroachment which O.R., Work Study, Industrial Engineering and the rest are felt to make. They are felt as taking away judgement and substituting a mathematical formula. They are felt as taking away the skill of an individual stores clerk or production control officer, which is often very considerable, and putting in its place a mechanical routine whose level of activity can be adjusted by the boss at will. The techniques they apply are also felt to be unworkable because they apply to normal situations, and nothing in one's own particular factory is ever normal. In this latter feeling the discretionary content of the job affected is often exaggerated so that the idea of replacement by a 'formula' is made to appear absurd.

Now these feelings are real enough and strong enough to militate not only against the use of more scientific management, but against the reader's own appreciation of its value, and particularly the value of O.R. which it is the purpose of this book to explain. Thus they must be explored and exposed as a fantasy.

A moment's thought will reveal that there is no more powerful apparatus in the world for making decisions than the human brain. Why burden it therefore with decisions which can be made by formulae? Why confine the power of judgement to choosing between this scheduling routine or that, or to gauging nicely when to replenish supplies of a particular item, when this judgement is sorely needed in assessing whether the whole scheduling policy is correct or whether the entire purchasing arrangements should be changed?

How many middle managers or managing directors have time to think? If you are a manager, and I hope you are because this book is addressed to you, keep a check for one day, or several if possible, on how you spend your time. Unless you are lucky, or very skilful (or already use O.R.!) you will find that much of your time is taken up in reviewing *ad hoc* decisions you took a few days ago and in taking more *ad hoc* decisions which again will turn up. How often do you say, 'If only I had time to think about that problem I could really get it out of my hair'?

13

But when someone else offers to do the thinking do you really welcome him? Or has the challenge of taking decisions, and it is a very welcome challenge to many people, so captivated you that the thought of relinquishing this power to the consistent operation of a settled routine is anathema? Or are you afraid that the freeing of judgement and discretion to operate at a higher level will find you wanting?

These questions need answering by anyone contemplating O.R. or similar aids to management. If these methods are seen as encroaching on a manager's prerogative, as reducing his discretion, as subjugating his staff to the dominance of a routine then the methods will not work. If, however, they are seen as providing means of freeing people for higher levels of discretion, as methods for replacing multitudinous conflicting *ad hoc* decisions by settled policies which managers have ample time to consider and review and as a way of ultimately securing more leisure and a higher standard of living for us all then they may succeed.

The scarcest commodity in industry is judgement. Let us not use it trivially.

Definition of Operational Research

Arthur Clarke, the science fiction writer, once defined O.R. as 'the art of winning wars without actually fighting'. This is certainly a tribute to the success of O.R. in World War II, but does not convey much to the industrial manager today.

In a recent book, Churchman, Ackoff and Arnoff suggested the following definition: 'O.R. is the application of scientific methods, techniques and tools to problems involving the operations of a system so as to provide those in control of the system with optimum solutions to the problems'.

The key to this definition is the phrase 'optimum solutions to the problems . . . involving the operations of a system'. In O.R. work a study is made of the system and not just separate components of it. Clearly the definition of the system is important because all systems in industry are part of a larger system and not all systems are appropriate ones for study by O.R. One of the first duties of an O.R. worker in an investigation is to make clear the boundaries of the system in which he is working, to ensure that it is appropriate for O.R. and to point out that the optimal solution is only being found for that particular system. If the optimal solution in the particular system has harmful repercussions on a larger system then the O.R. worker must not blind himself to this, but should endeavour to discover it and point out the need for investigation of the wider system.

For example an investigation into the optimum stock policy for a warehouse supplying spare parts ex stock resulted in an ordering routine being recommended which would have caused considerable fluctuation in the demand on the adjoining factory for manufacture of the spare parts. This would certainly not have been an optimum policy as far as the factory was concerned. The need for incorporating both the factory and the warehouse into the system being studied was recognised by the O.R. worker and the investigation proceeded.

The type of system with which O.R. is properly concerned will emerge to a certain extent in the course of the book and will be discussed more fully in the conclusion. Broadly speaking, however, the systems are those concerned with the capacity of the company to do work and with the programme needed to achieve the required amount of work.

Thus O.R. is concerned with systems. In this way it differs from Work Study, which is in general concerned with routines, particularly manual and clerical routines. Work Study as its name implies, aims at minimization of physical effort. Operational Research is used for optimization of planning effort.

Two examples of how O.R. and Work Study differ and yet fit in together can be given.

A system for quoting prices to customers was under review in a jobbing firm. The Sales Organization received customers' enquiries, passed them on to the Production Engineering Department (P.E.D.), who estimated what the part would cost to produce and then sent this estimate to the Sales Organization, who quoted the customer a price. Substantial delays occurred between the Sales Organization receiving an enquiry and sending a quotation. The Work Study Department examined the paper work routines and was able to simplify them and speed them up considerably, but there still remained a delay in the P.E.D. estimating section because the estimators had too much to do.

The particular estimating system was then studied by the O.R. Department, using queueing theory, which will be described later. The resulting calculations showed how many estimators would need to be employed and how their work should be organized to ensure on the one hand that no estimate would take longer than four hours to complete and on the other hand that no estimator would spend long periods in idleness. The O.R. Department then went on to study the entire system embracing the Sales Organization and the P.E.D., and evolved techniques whereby delays could be reduced still further.

In the second example a machine shop was set up for producing varying quantities of similar articles. The methods of machining and the work handling and paper work routines were evolved by the Production Engineering and Work Study Departments. The O.R. Department was called in to assist in establishing the optimum size of the machine shop, the number of machines and operators required, the optimum production scheduling methods and so on.

In both examples O.R. is seen to be concerned with the planning of the whole system to meet a given objective; Work Study is used for minimizing the effort taking place within the system.

By now it should be clearer what O.R. is and what it aims to do. Before the techniques of O.R. are discussed, however, it is worthwhile discussing the relationship of O.R. to Industrial Engineering, Management Accountancy and Organization and Methods, which claim the ear of management as powerfully as O.R. These three disciplines are concerned with the efficient use of the assets of a firm. Industrial Engineering with its physical assets, Management Accountancy with its financial assets, and Organization and Methods with its clerical and administrative assets. In this way they link up with O.R. in a similar way to Work Study. When O.R. is concerned with the optimization of a system in which the use of physical assets is the criterion of performance, then the relationship between O.R. and Industrial Engineering is as close as O.R. and Work Study in the above examples. Similarly, when the main criterion of the performance of a system is financial, there is a close co-operation between O.R. and Management Accounting. All five aids however perform distinct services to management. There should be no rivalry between them and in a well-run organization there should be no confusion as to their roles.

Some O.R. men have done a great disservice to the discipline by claiming it as an all-embracing method of solving any industrial problems by scientific methods. This is nonsense and should be recognized as such. Advocacy of this sort will only frighten managers or make them contemptuous of the wild claims. Operational Research will be used to its fullest extent in industry when and only when people know precisely what it is, understand its scope and limitations, and have convincing demonstrations of what it can do.

What Operational Research does

Given then that there is a system which may not be operating in an optimum manner, what is it that O.R. can do? What is it that O.R. brings to the situation which Work Study, Management Accounting and the rest do not bring? After all, although these techniques do not usually look at the system as a whole, and are not usually required to, there seems to be no reason why they should not do so. In that event of course one may ask what O.R. brings to the situation that the intelligent manager, who is always trying to look at the system as a whole, does not bring?

To answer this question it is probably useful to go a little into the history of O.R. Although (if one really tried) one could probably discover elements of O.R. in the military work of Archimedes and of some of the scientists who worked for Napoleon, and certainly of some of the scientists in World War I, it was really in World War II that it began to establish itself as a separate discipline.

When the British Government, anxious not to waste resources in the years of total war following Dunkirk, banded together groups of scientists to assist field commanders in solving strategic and tactical problems, it caused biologists to examine problems in electronics, physicists to observe movements of men rather than movements of molecules, mathematicians to examine how probability theory could influence men's survival and chemists to study equilibria in systems other than chemical ones. Similar work was being done under the Chief Scientist of the U.S. War Dept.

From all this work there arose the realization that techniques for studying systems in one discipline could be used with success in solving problems in systems outside that discipline.

Communication within a command or a unit exhibited symptoms similar to those which had been studied in telephone circuits. The control of an operation involving men and machines needed the same requirements for its success as did the servo-mechanisms of an aircraft.

17

The delays in unloading ships at ports were similar to the delays in waiting for calls at telephone exchanges, which had been studied for many years.

All these and other examples showed that there was a need for a technology in the study of systems which could draw from experience in the biological, physical, chemical and engineering sciences and utilize this experience in a wider sphere. This common technology is the technology of O.R.

One characteristic of O.R. therefore is that it is inter-disciplinary. It draws on techniques from biology, physics, chemistry, mathematics, economics, and so on and distils from among these techniques the ones which apply in the system being studied. Thus it is not surprising to find in an O.R. team men who have qualified in many different subjects and who can share their experience in pursuit of a common aim.

I must be careful, however, to avoid giving the impression that O.R. is techniques-bound, that it searches around for a known poultice to clap on to a management ache. This is becoming more and more true of many situations of course. This book will describe many techniques which can be applied, with modification, in well-known types of problem with a good chance of success. But this is not the whole of O.R. Above all, O.R. is an attitude of mind. The attitude of mind of an enquiring scientist who is not content with accepting a system as it is, but who wants to analyse it, find out what makes it tick, see how it responds to stimuli and encourage it to evolve in the best direction.

In the best O.R. work the technique for solving the problem arises from a study of the problem and is usually a new technique to be added to those in the O.R. worker's locker for use in similar problems elsewhere. With the other management aids the techniques for solving particular problems have usually been standardized and do not need to be evolved during the course of an investigation.

Now this description of O.R. may send a shiver down the spine of many a manager. A manager has to operate his systems willy-nilly. Work must be got out, goods produced, despatched, sold and paid for. This usually needs the full-time attention of a competent staff, comfortable in the working of an established procedure, knowing all the snags, confident in the way in which other people's work fits into their own. If some crazy scientist comes monkeying around with this scheme, what is going to happen? The basis of all scientific work is experimentation. Experimentation is just what apparently cannot be done with administrative systems.

The resolution of this impasse is a major conceptual contribution of O.R. This is the second hurdle over which I and my readers must leap. The first if you remember was that O.R. did not deprive managers of discretion, it freed them for higher levels of judgement. The second is that O.R. does not experiment with the system itself, it experiments with a model of the system.

This concept of model is very important and I will elaborate on it. By model is meant not necessarily a physical representation of the system such as a scale model which architects may make before finalizing the design of a building. The model in O.R. may be a mathematical formula or some other abstract representation which behaves in a similar way to the system being studied.

Let me give a very simple example of a mathematical model.

Suppose you are throwing a party and have £10 to spend. Then whatever you spend on food and on drink must not total more than £10. If you spend £6 on food you cannot spend more than £4 on drink and so on. The mathematical model for this is

$$x+y \leqslant 10$$

where x and y are the amounts, in pounds, spent on food and drink respectively and the symbol $\leqslant$ means 'less than or equal to'. Thus if x is £2, y must be less than or equal to £8 and so on. The model

$$x+y \leqslant 10$$

not only expresses the system you are examining more concisely than can be done in words, but it has the same properties and can be experimented on. You can say, 'If I spend £4 on food (x) then I cannot spend more than £6 on drink (y).' This is a simpler method of exploring the situation than actually spending £4 on food and finding that you had only £6 left for drink.

Now you may say, 'But this is ridiculous, this is just simple arithmetic, there's no nonsense about mathematical models needed here.' Just so, but stop and think. When you are using simple arithmetic you are still using a model of the situation. Because you think in terms of pounds, shillings and pence in working out your change from the tobacconist or calculating if you can afford that holiday in Spain you are not actually dealing in pounds, shillings and pence. You do not have the money in your hand to count out. You are using a model to explore different possibilities of the real situation and choosing the best results.

Very often of course the result is not what the model predicted. I would like to meet the genius whose holiday cost him just what he thought it would, but unless things went drastically wrong and some important factor was missed out of the model, such as the air fare or the cost of living abroad, then there is no doubt that the model was useful and even necessary to come to a decision.

The advantage of the model $x+y \leqslant 10$ over simple arithmetic is that more complex variations may be introduced and analysed readily. Suppose you said, 'I do not want to spend more than £10 and yet the drink must cost twice as much as the food.' The model of this situation is then the simultaneous expression

$$x+y \leqslant 10$$
$$y = 2x$$

This situation can then be analysed readily to reveal that x must lie between 0 and £3 6s. 8d. and y must be twice whatever x is. You then know that, with the conditions you have stated, you cannot spend more than £3 6s. 8d. on food. This kind of model, on a more elaborate scale, is used in linear programming.

This is the way an O.R. team works. It studies the situation, constructs a model of the system, usually mathematical or of similar abstraction, experiments on it to find the optimum performance and recommends this to the manager. He may then be reluctant to implement a change because the model is more sophisticated and hence less easy to understand than the simple accounting arithmetic that we are all used to, or because the more complex the real system the less likely is it that a model can represent it exactly; or because the consequences of making a bad change in a system are often very serious.

This is very natural. This is why O.R. workers must take great pains to explain their work. This is why O.R. men must often be content with tackling simple problems until confidence in their ability to construct a viable model and produce the correct results from experiments on it has grown in their superiors and colleagues. But when this stage has been reached, when men in charge of enterprises can feel able to examine some of their most complex systems and explore the possibilities of their evolution with a hitherto unknown and unsuspected freedom, then the fruits of such endeavour can be very great indeed.

I must not leave behind the impression, however, that O.R. has a message only for managers. It also has a message for Work Study men, Industrial Engineers, Management Accountants and other staff functionaries. Operational Research, as its name implies is *research*. Its practitioners are constantly seeking new ways of analysing situations, of understanding systems. Some of the techniques they evolve should very properly be incorporated into the body of knowledge of the other disciplines. Some very good examples of how this may be achieved are contained in *Operational Research and the Social Sciences* published by Tavistock Publications in 1966.

Work Study is beginning to make effective use of statistical methods, Management Accounting can fruitfully employ linear programming, Industrial Engineers are finding queueing theory of considerable assistance. This is as it should be. All will profit if workers in these fields regard O.R. not as a rival but as a co-partner and a source of refreshment.

REFERENCES

CHURCHMAN, C. W., ACKOFF, R. L., and ARNOFF, E. L. *Introduction to Operations Research*. Wiley (1957)

JAQUES, ELLIOTT. *Measurement of Responsibility*. Tavistock Publications (1956)

Other useful general books to read are:

MCCLOSKEY, J. F., and TREFETHEN, F. N. *Operations Research for Management*, Part I. Johns Hopkins Press (1954)

MCCLOSKEY, J. F., and COPPINGER, J. M. *Operations Research for Management*, Part II. Johns Hopkins Press (1956)

A detailed discussion of the relationship between Operational Research and Work Study, together with some asides on other management aids, has been given by A. Battersby in a paper entitled 'The use of Established O.R. Techniques in Work Study' published in *Work Study and Management*, September, 1963.

PART II: OPERATIONAL RESEARCH TECHNIQUES

For nothing goes for sense, or light,
That will not with old rules jump right,
As if rules were not in the schools
Derived from truth, but truth from rules.

SAMUEL BUTLER: *Hudibras*

Operational Research techniques are continually being evolved. Indeed as stated earlier, the O.R. worker must often avoid the pitfalls of existing techniques in maintaining his enquiring experimental attitude of mind. Certain techniques have, however, now been used in many situations so successfully with only minor modifications on each occasion that the responsible O.R. man must always consider these techniques first in the given situations because, after all, he is paid to produce results, not to satisfy his own intellectual curiosity (although the pay-off for allowing the latter is often very high).

These techniques will now be described to give a clearer indication of just how O.R. works and the results it has had. Many of these techniques are derived from mathematical statistics which is still one of the most powerful tools in the O.R. approach. This is necessarily so, because one common property of industrial systems is their variability and mathematical statistics is the method of handling the problem of variability. The other techniques to be described are linear programming, queueing theory, Monte Carlo and simulation methods, stock and production control models, decision theory and game theory, operational gaming, cybernetics, information theory and evolutionary operation.

22.

These techniques will be described in non-mathematical language as far as is possible.

Mathematical statistics

Most of us are familiar with the ideas of probability. In tossing coins one expects heads and tails to occur with equal frequency, so we say that the probability of a head or a tail is $\frac{1}{2}$. In throwing an ordinary die we can see that the chance of getting any particular number at the first throw is 1 in 6. If a penny always came down heads or a die always came down with the five uppermost it would not take many throws before we began to suspect that all was not as it should be.

We would probably doubt the genuineness of the penny after five heads had occurred in the first five throws. Calculation shows that this sequence of heads could occur *by chance* once in thirty-two times, so it is not completely out of the question that the penny is unbiased. A probability of $\frac{1}{32}$ is small enough, however, to make us suspicious. If we threw the penny for another five times and had a further five heads then we would have no doubt that the penny was biased, because 10 heads in a row only occur by chance 1 in 1024 times and we all know from our experience with football pools that this kind of chance event does not happen to us, because these odds are similar to those of winning a worth-while dividend in any one year.

Mathematical statistics provides means of calculating the probability of chance events in situations much more complicated than those of tossing pennies or throwing dice.

These calculations enable the O.R. worker to say whether observations obtained in real life, or in an experiment on a model, really show that things have been changed or whether what was thought to be an important result could actually have occurred by chance.

The example on p. 24 illustrates this. Suppose the daily output of two particular machines varied over a period in the way indicated.

At first sight it looks as though production on the first machine was higher than on the second, but can we be sure that if further observations were taken that the difference would be maintained? There were, we must note, four occasions on which the output of the second machine was higher than the average of the first and an equal number of occasions in which the output of the first machine was lower than the average of the second.

Machine A	Machine B
107	94
94	111
122	94
100	96
107	92
106	80
115	109
91	89
112	85
120	114
106	97
90	94
116	96
102	98
118	93
94	113
Average = 106	Average = 97

In other words, could the difference between the output of the two machines have occurred by chance in the same way that five heads may occur by chance in the throwing of an unbiased coin, or is there sufficient evidence to justify the belief that there is a real difference in the behaviour of the two machines?

The methods of mathematical statistics enable us to calculate the probability of obtaining by chance this observed difference in machine behaviour if in fact there were no difference between the machines. This is clearly an important tool in O.R. because, as in all scientific and experimental work, it is necessary to distinguish between real and chance effects in order to make satisfactory progress.

In the above example the probability that the observed difference between the two machines could have occurred by chance has been calculated and was in fact only 1 in 25, therefore it would have been reasonable to assume that there was a real difference between the two machines. If a much smaller probability were required, because, say, it was very important to establish the reality of the difference, then it could be predicted that if 11 more trials were carried out on each machine and if the difference in performance persisted, then the probability that this difference was still due to chance would have fallen to 1 in 1,000.

Statistical methods can also guide the planning of experiments so that the optimum use is made of whatever data is obtained. The general principle of such techniques is to arrange that the data can be paired off in such a way that differences between the observations are emphasized. For instance, if the above data on machine behaviour had been obtained so that the results for A and B could be compared pair by pair as shown below, it will be seen that in every case machine A has a higher output than machine B, and more confidence can be placed in the assertion that machine A has consistently the higher output than was the case when the data could not be so arranged.

Machine A	Machine B
107	98
94	92
122	114
100	97
107	96
106	96
115	94
91	89
112	109
120	111
106	94
90	80
116	113
102	94
118	93
94	85

An example of the use of this pairing technique, not taken from O.R. because the background to such examples is often tedious to explain, but which may help to fix its value in the reader's mind, is in medical research. A number of patients may be selected for a trial of certain

25

drugs. Each patient is given one drug, and its effect observed, and then the same patients are given another drug, perhaps days later, and the effect observed again. The results may look like the ones below.

Number of hours sleep obtained by insomnious
patients after administration of drug

Patient No.	Drug A	Drug B
1	4·5	5·5
2	6·0	8·2
3	4·5	5·5
4	4·3	6·8
5	1·5	1·8
6	2·0	3·0
7	4·5	4·7
8	1·3	2·0

It can be seen that although the effectiveness of the drugs varied considerably from patient to patient, drug B was always better than drug A. Because of the variability from patient to patient the superiority of drug B would not have been at all clear if the drugs had been tried on two different groups of patients.

This is but a simple illustration of the use of statistical methods in enabling investigations to be planned so that maximum value is obtained from the data produced. Much more complex techniques are needed in more complicated situations, but sufficient has probably been said to illustrate their value in operational research. They serve three purposes, one is to enable real results to be distinguished from chance ones, another is to assist in the planning of investigations so that the maximum use is made of the results, and the third is to enable predictions to be made about the frequency with which certain numbers will occur, by chance, in particular situations. More will be said about this third use of statistical methods in the section on stock and production control models.

Some of the statistical methods used for interpreting data are relatively simple and quick to apply in particular circumstances. These are explained in more detail in Appendix I for those who wish to use them.

Linear programming

This is a technique which can be used in a situation where there are several products which can be made on each of several different machines and a programme is needed to decide which product shall be made on which machine in order to maximize output or minimize cost or satisfy some other criterion of efficiency. For example, in a forging shop there may be a mixture of old and new presses with different output rates and different costs. If there is a variety of jobs to be handled on these presses then the number of ways in which these jobs can be arranged may be enormous. For example, with 20 jobs to be arranged between 5 presses the total number of possible arrangements is 5^{20}, or one hundred million million. Not all of these will be worthy of consideration of course. Many combinations involving an excessive loading of jobs on to one press can be rejected from the calculation, but this still leaves a very large number of possibilities to be considered by the scheduling officer.

It is well known in fact that in this kind of situation the scheduling officer's job is a very skilled one, and is usually handled by men with long experience who have evolved some very adequate rules for deciding upon the optimum arrangement. Even so, they cannot possibly consider more than a fraction of the alternatives available, and some unsuspected optimum may well have escaped them.

Several other problems fall into this same category. Choosing the combination of widths into which to slit paper in order to minimize the amount of waste at the edges is one example which has been successfully tackled by Doig. So has the economic mixing of animal foodstuffs to meet certain specifications (Muir). Deciding which goods to send from which warehouse to which customer, or which tankers to send from which oil supply to which refineries are examples of the so-called 'Transportation problem' of linear programming which are in use (Garvin *et al.*). Other examples of its use in the oil industry have been given by Deam and by Caplin. Battersby has suggested its use in plant design. In cases where there is a choice of resources to be deployed to achieve a variety of different objects, linear programming can usually be employed to give the optimal solution with a relatively small amount of calculation.

A typical example which is in daily use in one company is the method of deciding which of several batches of bearing metal, recovered from the manufacturing operations in which surplus bearing metal is machined from the cast bearings, shall be used in making up fresh metal required by the foundry. Due to contamination and similar effects the composition of the recovered bearing metal differs from that of the required specification. It cannot therefore be used again directly but must either be sold or mixed with other metal to restore the correct composition.

If the metal is sold there is a book loss because the price given is less than the nominal value of the alloy. If the metal is kept for remixing but cannot be used for a long time, then a substantial amount of available capital may be tied up and additional storage costs incurred.

There are usually about 20 batches of recovered metal available for making up fresh metal required by the foundry, and so there is the problem of which melts to choose and in which proportion to use them.

This problem used to be tackled by an experienced chemist who spent nearly half his working day making the decisions. It is now solved by linear programming by a girl computer working at a desk-calculating machine for about two hours a day. The method is described by Morton, Kay and Duckworth.

No great savings were experienced initially when the linear programming method was introduced. The utilization of recovery melts was increased, however, by about 4 per cent and stock turnover was much more rapid because it was possible to explore the potentialities of all the available batches whereas the chemist with his slide rule tended to concentrate on the more obvious melts and the less amenable ones therefore accumulated. This reduction in stock is shown in Figure 3.

The chemist had been very able in his job, and had built up a good deal of experience over the years, so no spectacular savings occurred at first. In the following two years the superiority of linear programming over the old method was, however, clearly demonstrated by Wyatt. The system is very flexible and can adjust itself to changes in supply and demand very rapidly, whereas the previous technique, being necessarily built up on experience, was slow to change. In the motor industry recession of 1956 there was no building up of recovered metal stocks when the ratio of supply to demand changed. The calculations took the change into account and the increased proportion of recovered melts was immediately utilized, whereas in previous recessions quite high stocks had been built up before this change in conditions was allowed for in the calculations.

The linear programming method has enabled a bird's-eye view of

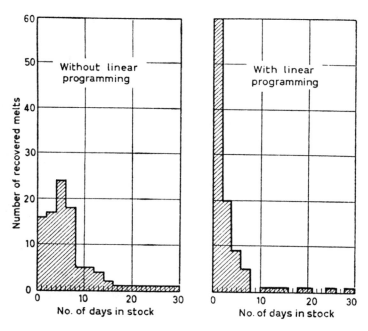

FIG. 3

Distribution of recovered melts by number of days in stock.

the process to be obtained. It is now clear which type of recovery melt can be used and which cannot. The latter are not allowed to remain in stock but are recommended for sale immediately. Certain restrictions on the use of recovered melts due to specification limitations were recognized and a recommendation to a B.S.I. Committee arising from this has borne fruit. The principle of linear programming can be illustrated with reference to this example of choosing the proportions of several alloys required to make up a new alloy economically. Suppose we have two recovered melts available with the following compositions:

Melt 1	*Melt 2*
2 parts copper	1 part copper
1 part nickel	3 parts nickel

There are 7 lb. of the first melt available and 6 lb. of the second, and we want to combine suitable proportions to make 10 lb. of a $50:50$ copper nickel alloy. Let us further assume that if we use the first alloy, instead of pure copper or pure nickel, we save $5d$. per lb., and if we use the second alloy we save $10d$. per lb. The problem is to use the two alloys in the proportion which will maximize our saving.

We want 10 lb. of a $50:50$ Cu/Ni alloy, so we need 5 lb. copper and 5 lb. nickel. If we let x_1 be the weight of the first alloy that we use, then the weight of copper it will contribute is $2x_1/3$. Similarly, if x_2 is the weight of the second alloy used, then the weight of copper it will contribute is $x_2/4$.

If z_1 is the weight of fresh copper we have to add, then the total weight of copper we use is

$$\frac{2x_1}{3} + \frac{x_2}{4} + z_1$$

But in our final alloy we must have 5 lb. of copper, so therefore we have our first equation,

$$\frac{2x_1}{3} + \frac{x_2}{4} + z_1 = 5. \tag{i}$$

Similarly, for nickel,

$$\frac{x_1}{3} + \frac{3x_2}{4} + z_2 = 5 \tag{ii}$$

where z_2 is the amount of fresh nickel added.

In addition, we know that x_1 cannot exceed 7 lb. and x_2 cannot exceed 6 lb. To obtain the greatest saving ($5d$. on x_1 and $10d$. on x_2) we must maximize

$$5x_1 + 10x_2.$$

This is the typical formulation of a linear programming problem. It will be noticed that there are two equations (i) and (ii) with four unknowns x_1, x_2, z_1 and z_2. Therefore they cannot be solved by normal methods for simultaneous equations. In addition, the unknowns must have non-negative values. In this case however, we can solve the problem graphically.

The equation $2x_1/3 + x_2/4 + z_1 = 5$ decribes the unshaded region in Figure 4 below.

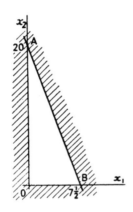

FIG. 4

The line AB has the equation $2x_1/3 + x_2/4 = 5$, and this represents the upper limit of the copper content required because we do not need more than 5 lb. of copper. The region on the right-hand side of AB is therefore shaded showing that we do not want to consider any points in this region. Similarly the parts below the line x_1 and to the left of the line x_2 are shaded because these regions represent *negative* values of x_1 and x_2, which we are certainly not interested in.

So the solution we want is somewhere in the triangle OAB. A similar triangle can be constructed for the nickel equation

$$\frac{x_1}{3} + \frac{3x_2}{4} + z_2 = 5$$

31

This is shown in Figure 5.

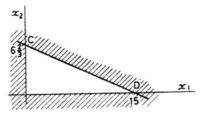

FIG. 5

where CD is the line

$$\frac{x_1}{3} + \frac{3x_2}{4} = 5$$

The limitation that x_1 cannot be more than 7 and x_2 cannot be more than 6 is shown in Figure 6.

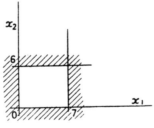

FIG. 6

The solution to our problem must therefore lie within the region common to Figures 4, 5 and 6, and this contains the infinite number of possible ways of mixing the two alloys from which we have to choose.

This region is shown in Figure 7.

Within that region we want to make

$$5x_1 + 10x_2 \text{ a maximum.}$$

The line XY is a line with the equation

$$5x_1 + 10x_2 = \text{a constant.}$$

32

We want to make this constant as large as possible so we move the line to the right (as indicated by the arrows and retaining the direction) as far as we can while still remaining within the area where we know the solution must lie. The furthest we can go is to the point W, which therefore represents the solution.

It can be seen that the solution is to use 6 lb. of x_1 (alloy 1) and 4 lb. of x_2 (alloy 2). No fresh copper or nickel is needed.

In actual linear programming problems there are more than two alternatives to consider and so the problems cannot usually be illustrated in two dimensions as this one can. To illustrate more complex problems in the same way would involve n-dimensional geometry.

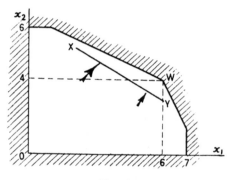

Fig. 7

Relatively simple computing techniques have been evolved for these complex problems. These are described by Charnes and others, Vajda and Gass.

This example illustrates the technique, however, and a little study of Figure 7 will show how altering the conditions alters the solution. If we make the amount of alloy 1 available less than 6 lb. for instance, it means that all of x_1 will be used and some extra of x_2 will be required but that the saving will no longer be as great as with the first solution. It is this kind of consideration which enables linear programming to survey the problem in all its aspects and explore the consequences of alternative solutions. The necessity for the functions to be linear has hitherto caused some restriction in the use of the techniques but recent research by Gould, among others, has shown that non-linear problems can be tackled by the method.

Queueing theory

We are all familiar with queues. If too many people arrive at a shop in a given time then a queue forms. Most factories are operated on the principle of having queues so that work can be continually fed into a department without the periods of idle time which might ensue if there were no queues. In this case a queue is a good thing, it helps to assist in economic planning of the department's work. If the queue becomes too large, however, difficulties arise. The pace of work may be stepped up to reduce the queue and unless the increased pace is within the capacity of the department, efficiency may in fact fall, leading to the queue being lengthened rather than shortened.

Priorities may be resorted to and this can be very dangerous because the transfer of jobs to a higher place in the queue only results in the average waiting time of all remaining jobs lengthening, which may increase the need for further priorities, and so a cycle of panic measures sets in.

For service-giving departments, such as millwrights, a queue of work can be a very inefficient thing to have. If too many machines are needing repair at the same time, the consequences can be serious.

A mathematical theory of queues has been developed which enables O.R. workers to calculate for any given situation what kind of queue will result and how long the items will have to wait before service. Certain conclusions of this theory are sufficiently concise to be worth stating here.

In the first place the probability of a queue varies more or less directly with the proportion of time that the service provided is going to be in demand. Thus if a service is used to 80 per cent of its capacity the probability that there will be a queue is about 8 out of 10, i.e. in 8 out of 10 calls on that service we shall have to wait before being served. (Although this is only strictly true for a queueing system with a single server, random arrivals and a distribution of service times known as negative exponential, it is approximately true for most common systems.)

This is something that we all observe in practice. If we frequently visit a shop with several assistants and we find that we are always

34

served immediately, then we notice that some of the assistants have no customers to see to. If on the other hand we call in at a busy news-agent's every morning and there is only one man serving behind the counter we almost invariably have to wait a while.

The meaning of this relationship between service capacity and queue probability is that if we carefully plan a service department so that it has just enough capacity to meet expected demand then we can expect a queue to exist at all times and to grow continually.

If on the other hand we want it to meet every demand almost im-mediately, then we must expect it to spend about half its time in idle-ness. This explains the perpetual headache of the man in charge of such a department – how to arrange things so he can give a reasonable service and yet at the same time keep his men fully occupied. In this situation the man who keeps the odd painting job up his sleeve is not really making work for his men, he is ensuring that his department can give a good service and yet not appear to be over-staffed.

The other main conclusion which emerges from the theory of queues is that the more haphazard the arrivals the greater is the customer's expected waiting time. This is because with haphazard arrivals a time may come when no demands are made for a long period. That time is lost from the system and when subsequently a bunch of arrivals occurs it takes a long time for the system to catch up and disperse the resulting back-log.

To ensure that reasonably rapid service can be provided therefore it is advisable to arrange that the service-giving department – or pro-duction unit – is only loaded, on average, to about 80 % of its ultimate capacity (including full overtime, etc.) and that the demands on it are made as uniformly as possible.

This is common sense, of course, and most managers do not need an operational research study to tell them this. There are many situa-tions, however, in which we may wish to know precisely how long items may have to wait in a queue for a given service capacity so that we can decide whether to provide extra capacity, at extra cost, or let the items wait a little longer and risk the losses which may arise from giving a less satisfactory service.

Here again the O.R. worker can set up a mathematical model of the system and study its properties and so learn something of the likely behaviour of the system in real life. For solving queueing problems mathematically an expression known as the traffic intensity is used. This is the demand divided by the capacity, or more precisely – the mean service time divided by the mean interval between successive arrivals. It is usually given the Greek symbol ρ. The calculation of the traffic intensity for any system is relatively simple. The intervals between the arrivals of jobs or customers or whatever it is that is being served is measured and the average of these intervals determined. A good method of making sure that an accurate measure of the average has been obtained and not one that has been influenced unduly by one or two unusually long or short intervals is to plot the cumulative average against the number of arrivals as in the following example.

Suppose the arrival intervals, to the nearest minute, were

5, 4, 10, 6, 3, 2, 6, 4, 8, 15, 2, 5, 4, 6, 8, 7, 3, 5, 2, 6, 8, 7, 4, 3, 2, 6, 7, 5, 3, 4, 6, 5, 8, 4.

The cumulative totals, obtained by adding the first two intervals and then the first three and so on are

9, 19, 25, 28, 30, 36, 40, 48, 63, 65, 70, 74, 80, 88, 95, 98, 103, 105, 111, 119, 126, 130, 133, 135, 141, 148, 153, 156, 160, 166, 171, 179, and 183.

The cumulative averages obtained by dividing all the cumulative totals by the number of intervals making up each total are as follows

$$\frac{9}{2}, \frac{19}{3}, \frac{25}{4}, \frac{28}{5}, \frac{30}{6}, \frac{36}{7}, \frac{40}{8}, \frac{48}{9}, \frac{63}{10}, \frac{65}{11}, \frac{70}{12}, \frac{74}{13}, \frac{80}{14}, \frac{88}{15}, \frac{95}{16}, \frac{98}{17}, \frac{103}{18}, \frac{105}{19}, \frac{111}{20},$$

$$\frac{119}{21}, \frac{126}{22}, \frac{130}{23}, \frac{133}{24}, \frac{135}{25}, \frac{141}{26}, \frac{148}{27}, \frac{153}{28}, \frac{156}{29}, \frac{160}{30}, \frac{166}{31}, \frac{171}{32}, \frac{179}{33} \text{ and } \frac{183}{34}$$

or in decimal notation

4·5; 6·3; 6·2; 5·6; 5·0; 5·1; 5·0; 5·3; 6·3; 5·9; 5·8; 5·7; 5·7; 5·9; 5·9; 5·8; 5·7; 5·5; 5·6; 5·7; 5·7; 5·6; 5·5; 5·4; 5·4; 5·5; 5·5; 5·4; 5·3; 5·3; 5·3; 5·4; 5·4.

When these cumulative averages are plotted against the number of intervals the result is shown in Figure 8. This fluctuates a little at first but then settles down to a fairly steady figure of 5·4 minutes. This is the value to take as the average interval between arrivals.

The average service time can be found in a similar way. For example it may be 4·5 minutes. Then in this instance the traffic intensity would be

$$\frac{4·5}{5·4} = 0·8\dot{3}\dot{3}.$$

Now it has been shown that in simple queueing systems where there

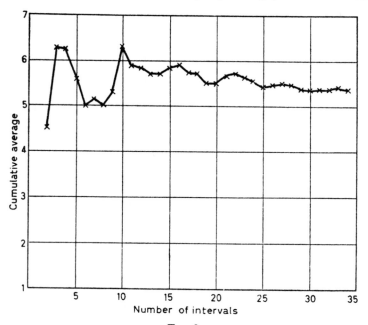

FIG. 8

Cumulative average plotted against number of intervals.

is only one service point and hence only one queue, as in the case of the tobacconist's counter or of a single man working a machine in a millwright's shop, the customer's average waiting time (including the time being served), again measured over a fairly long period, is

$$\frac{1}{1-\rho} \times \text{mean service time.}$$

This relationship only applies strictly in cases where both the arrival intervals and service times vary at random with a particular kind of distribution known as the negative exponential distribution. This distribution is very common in queueing situations, however, and so the relationship can be used in most cases.

Thus in the particular example we have worked out the mean waiting time would be

$$\frac{1}{1-0\cdot833} \times 4\cdot5 = 27 \text{ minutes.}$$

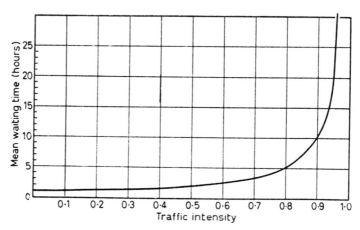

FIG. 9

The effect of traffic intensity on mean waiting time in a single server system with mean service time one hour.

This might be tolerable, but if the demand increased so that the mean arrival interval became 5 minutes, then the mean waiting time increases quite sharply to 45 minutes.

In fact with traffic intensities above 0·8 the mean waiting time rapidly increases with any increase in traffic intensity, as shown in Figure 9.

This shows how bottlenecks can arise with a slight increase in demand in systems where the traffic intensity is high. This congestion may sometimes be very slow to build up, as is shown in Figure 10, which is reproduced from a paper by Robinson. The traffic intensity was 0·96 and it was not until 250 arrivals had been dealt with that the waiting time became excessive.

Equally, however, the congestion may be very slow to disperse unless the traffic intensity is reduced very considerably below 1·0, by excessive overtime working or by employing extra servers or machines. It is therefore wise not to allow the traffic intensity of any servicing point to approach unity unless means are available for reducing it very considerably if necessary. The likely bottlenecks in any complex system can be estimated by computing the traffic intensities of each

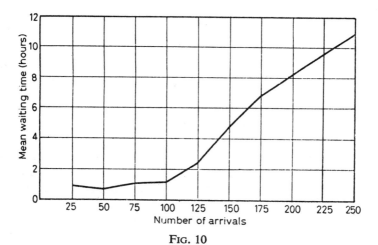

FIG. 10

Increase in mean waiting time with time.

service point and noting that those in excess of 0·8 are likely to cause trouble.

In the paper by Robinson, already referred to, an estimating section of a Production Engineering Department found itself occasionally unable to meet requests at short notice, even though its traffic intensity was only usually around 0·72. This problem was solved by having a third estimator on call to deal with emergencies. His presence lowered the traffic intensity to 0·48 and enabled a very rapid service to be provided when necessary. He was, of course, employed on other work when not required for estimating.

By employing the mathematics of queueing a manager is able to assess the probable efficiency of a system in terms of its service-providing or productive capacity, to estimate the likely bottlenecks and plan to eliminate them and, if queues are inevitable, to calculate their likely length so that he can make provision for storing the items while they are waiting for service. In this respect queueing problems are linked with production and stock control problems to be considered later.

The literature on queues is now very voluminous. A comprehensive bibliography of 700 papers has been prepared by Doig. A good introductory book to read is the one by Morse.

Monte Carlo and simulation methods

Some systems are so complicated as to defy mathematical analysis, or else the data available cannot be expressed in mathematical form. This situation is solved by use of the so-called Monte Carlo methods. If this conjures up a picture of dice throwing and roulette spinning it is meant to, because this is just how the O.R. worker imitates the occurrence of chance events in the system he is studying.

As an example, suppose an event being observed has a probability of 1 in 6 of occurring in any half-hour period. Then, to build up a picture of how the event might actually occur in practice, we divide the working day into half-hour periods, throw a die for each of these periods and each time a six comes uppermost (assuming the die to be unbiased) record that the event has occurred. More complex probabilities can be imitated by means of other devices such as a table of random numbers, and any system can be 'lived through' painlessly on a piece of paper and all the possible outcomes understood before the scheme is tried out in practice on the factory floor.

This technique was used, for example, to decide if a certain small factory had enough external telephone lines. There were in fact three lines and the factory manager became convinced that all three lines were in use so much that some customers, despairing of always hearing the engaged tone when they rang, would go elsewhere for their goods. For a period of a fortnight the telephone operator noted the amount of time that one, two and three lines were occupied and charts such as the one shown in Figure 11 were produced, which showed the proportion of time all three lines were occupied. By choosing times at random

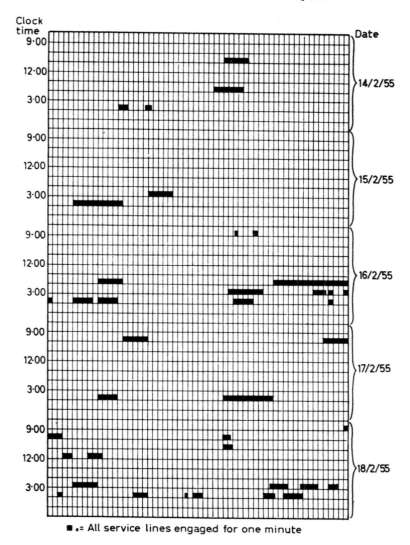

.∎ = All service lines engaged for one minute

FIG. 11

Graph showing time and duration of 'all service lines engaged'.

41

at which customers might have telephoned, the O.R. worker was able to record the proportion of times that the customer would have been connected immediately, or, if he failed the first time, the probability that he was successful the second time. As can be seen from the table below, these probabilities were so high, nearly 100 per cent in fact, that the factory manager realized his original impressions were unfounded and that no extra telephone lines were needed.

TABLE 1

Chance of caller's acceptance in a single call
during peak period 3–5 p.m.

Date	Chance (in 100)
14th	$97\frac{1}{2}$
15th	$87\frac{1}{2}$
16th	78
17th	88
18th	$77\frac{1}{2}$
21st	100
22nd	80
23rd	96
24th	100
25th	100

It is common in O.R. work to find that people's first impression of a problem is not the correct one and one of the tasks of an O.R. worker is to understand for himself what the real problem is. A very useful technique for a manager who feels he has a congestion problem and which can help to establish if the problem is real or not, is the method of random observation studies, often called ratio delay by production engineers.

It may be reported for example that a certain machine in a factory is always a bottleneck. To establish the facts for himself the manager should merely note, each time he walks through the factory, which, except for meal times, will probably be at random intervals, whether the machine is in use or not. At the end of a fortnight when he consults his record, he may be surprised to find that the machine is by no means in constant use as had been claimed. Armed with such facts, collected without special effort, the manager will be on the way to sorting out the real problem.

Complex simulation problems can be tackled by means of an electronic computer. This can perform repetitive operations very swiftly and so 'live through' many weeks of experience in a factory situation in a few hours. One such large-scale simulation has been carried out in the Glacier Metal Co.

A new machine shop was being set up to manufacture a certain product which needed a short delivery time if it was to sell in adequate quantity. The manufacturing techniques and machining times for this product were well known, but it was necessary to determine as accurately as possible how many machines and men would be required to achieve a given throughput time with a known level of input. It was necessary also to determine whether men were likely to be idle for long periods if the input to the shop fluctuated, so that other work could be planned for them.

In other words what was required was a model of the machine shop on which the manager could experiment by changing the number and type of machines, the number of men employed and the input and see what happened to work in progress, throughput time, labour utilization and machine utilization, so he could see where bottlenecks developed and plan how to eliminate them. The system was too complex for a mathematical model to be constructed and the whole shop was therefore imitated by means of an electronic computer.

To simplify the operation somewhat a 'first come, first served' production scheduling rule was assumed. That is each job as it entered the simulated shop was dealt with in turn and as each job finished on one machine it was placed on the end of the queue for the next machine. There were no priorities.

This is not an unrealistic picture. Priority rules, as every production controller knows, are the machine-shop manager's nightmare. For efficient working of a production unit it should be possible to produce everything within the time required on a 'first come, first served' basis. There must be exceptions of course, as when a particular customer requires very quick delivery but complex scheduling plans just will not work on the shop floor, where machine breakdowns and absence of key operators through illness are not unknown. Once a tight scheduling scheme is thrown out of joint by one such mischance it ceases to be operable.

It was decided that this shop would operate as far as possible on a 'first come, first served' basis and one of the purposes of the simulation was to discover what the throughput time of various categories of parts was under this regime so that their scheduling and delivery dates could be arranged accordingly.

What the electronic computer did therefore was to take each job as it entered the 'shop', assign it to its first machine, and transfer it to its second machine when it had moved to the head of the queue on its first machine and had been 'operated on' for the appropriate length of time. This was done for each job on each machine until it emerged from the last machine as a 'completed part'. It should be stated that not every 'job' went on every 'machine' nor did each 'job' visit the same number of 'machines'. The total time taken from entering the shop to leaving it was measured, and at frequent intervals the length of queue on each machine was also measured. The number of men employed and idle at any given time was also available.

Every time a man completed the processing of a job on a particular machine, a priority rule determined whether he should start on the next job waiting in the queue or move to another machine. Two-shift working was incorporated; the machines which gained or lost men at each change of shift were decided by the priority rule.

The manner in which the computer was used to simulate the operation of the machine shop will probably be clear if a simplified example is described. Consider a machine shop with six machines and three operators. The accompanying tables show the times at which jobs are scheduled to be completed on the machines. Times are measured from the moment when the simulation started and are quoted as integral numbers, where the unit of time is one-hundredth of an hour.

First, the computer is set to examine the jobs waiting at the heads of all the queues in order to locate the job that will be completed first. In the case shown, machine C will be chosen first because 13,049 is the smallest number in column 1. The action now taken by the computer is, in effect, to move forward through time until it reaches the moment quoted, i.e. 13,049 units of time. This, of course, means that the operation on machine C will have been completed, so the job processed on this machine is transferred to the end of the queue of the next machine specified in the production sequence. This, say, is machine F and the job enters the third position in the queue. Suppose the time required to complete the particular operation on this machine is 542 units; then the new completion time for this job is derived by adding 542 to the completion time given for the job immediately before it in the queue. The new completion time therefore becomes $13{,}901 + 542 = 14{,}443$. This figure is seen in Table 3. The queue of work on machine C is now moved forward, the number 13,627 coming to the head of the queue.

TABLE 2

Position in queue: Machine:	(1)	(2)	(3)	(4)	(5)
A	2^{37}	2^{37}	2^{37}	2^{37}	2^{37}
B	13,425	2^{37}	2^{37}	2^{37}	2^{37}
C	13,049	13,627	14,308	2^{37}	2^{37}
D	$2^{37} + 13{,}290$	$2^{37} + 13{,}543$	2^{37}	2^{37}	2^{37}
E	2^{37}	2^{37}	2^{37}	2^{37}	2^{37}
F	13,614	13,901	2^{37}	2^{37}	2^{37}

TABLE 3

Position in queue: Machine	(1)	(2)	(3)	(4)	(5)
A	2^{37}	2^{37}	2^{37}	2^{37}	2^{37}
B	13,425	2^{37}	2^{37}	2^{37}	2^{37}
C	13,627	14,308	2^{37}	2^{37}	2^{37}
D	$2^{37} + 13{,}726$	$2^{37} + 13{,}979$	2^{37}	2^{37}	2^{37}
E	2^{37}	2^{37}	2^{37}	2^{37}	2^{37}
F	13,614	13,901	14,443	2^{37}	2^{37}

Only three operators are available to work the six machines; three machines must, therefore, be idle. Obviously, when the computer is scanning column 1 to detect the lowest number, it must be prevented from choosing a machine that is not manned. This is done by adding a very large number, 2^{37}, to the completion times of all jobs on unmanned machines. This number also appears in all positions in the queues not occupied by jobs. In this way it is possible to make the computer ignore all machines having no work (machines A and E) and also unmanned machines (machine D).

If the computer moved forward 436 units of time to get to 13,049, then 436 units must be added to the completion times of all jobs waiting in the queue of unmanned machines. This has been done for the two jobs waiting at machine D and the new completion times are quoted in Table 3. All is now ready for the process to be repeated. The computer will search column 1 for the earliest completion time and the procedure will be gone through again.

A system of priorities is necessary to determine how the men shall be allocated to the machines. In real life this is a matter of intuition, but because the computer is incapable of exercising this faculty, a rule had to be found that would appear reasonable to workshop supervisors and be capable of being programmed. The obvious rule of allocating men to the machines with the longest queues would penalize those jobs going on lightly loaded machines. The solution adopted therefore is to set a criterion of priority for each job by assessing the difference between the scheduled completion time for the job on its current machine and the time it joined the queue for that machine.

Whenever a job is completed on a machine the operator is sent to a central reserve. The computer then scans the jobs at the heads of the queues of the unmanned machines and allocates the man to the machine with the job possessing the highest priority on the basis just quoted. Of course, the machine the operator has just left has become inactive and, if it has a queue of work, it will often reclaim him. In this event, no break occurs in the operation of the particular machine because the computer does not move forward in time while it performs the allocation procedure.

In order that one programmed routine may be able to cope with the arrival of jobs at the machine shop as well as with movements from machine to machine, two special 'arrival machines' are included in the model of the situation. Each arrival machine has room for a queue of 48 jobs. If 96 jobs are placed in the queues of these machines the normal programmed procedure will see to it that they are fed into the workshop at the right times. A continuous flow of work is maintained by repeatedly feeding in a fixed sequence of jobs.

A Ferranti Pegasus computer was used to perform the machine shop simulation. The data which need to accompany a job on its tour of the machine shop can be contained in two registers of the Pegasus information store. Consequently, to provide sufficient information storage capacity for 48 separate jobs to be held in a queue, 96 consecutive registers were earmarked. (The number 48 has no particular virtue: it is dictated primarily by the storage capacity available within the computer.) A maximum number of 40 machines was envisaged for the workshop, so 3,840 registers were needed to hold their queues. Data which did not need to accompany the job on the journey from machine to machine were recorded in another part of the information store. Examples of such data are the reference numbers of the machines needed for the complete manufacturing cycle, arranged in sequence, together with the preparation times for each operation and the machining times.

Tables 2 and 3 illustrate the type of data recorded in the first register. The second register contained the priority value allocated to each job, the job number and the number of machines that the job has visited. Without this last information it would not have been possible to look up the details of the next operation to be performed.

The simulation of the machine shop incorporated a means of periodically increasing and decreasing the number of men working in the shop. In this way shift working could be simulated. Both the length of the shifts and the distribution of manpower could be varied. Extra men were added to the reserve of free men on changing from night shift to day shift. These men were then allocated to machines, in accordance with the priority system already described, until either no more men were free or all machines with queues of work had received men. Conversely, the change from day shift to night shift involved first, the removal of men from the reserve of free men; then, if further men had to go, they were removed, one by one, from the active machines with the lowest priority jobs.

Every time the computer performed an action, a test was made to see whether it was time to print a report on the queues of work at each machine. These reports showed the forward load for each machine, that is the completion time of the final job in the queue minus the present time.

A simplified flow chart showing the main features of the programme appears in Figure 12. The computer performed this cycle of operations approximately once per second. It can be seen that during a run most of the programme was used repeatedly. Those parts which were used

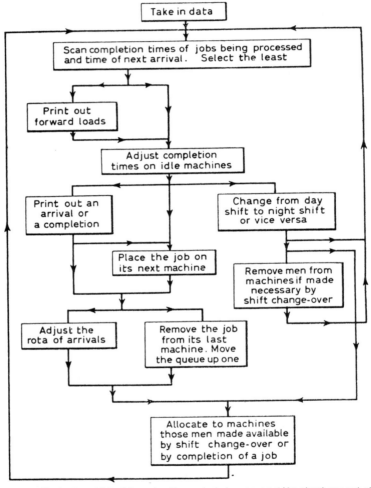

Note: The tests which determine the route taken around the chart are not shown

FIG. 12

once only were concerned with the introduction of data at the start of a run or with stopping the computer when either a job was about to be loaded on to a machine that already had 48 jobs in its queue or a certain length of time had been simulated, for example, 2,000 working hours. Incidentally, the computer could simulate 10 hours' operation of the machine shop in one minute.

Thus the model in the electronic computer was able to provide all the data that the manager needed to assess the necessary size of the

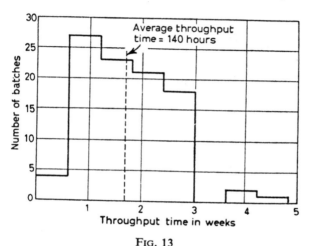

Fig. 13

Distribution of throughput time.

machine shop and gave him advance information of the conditions he was likely to meet. A fuller description of this particular simulation is given by Wyatt.

Typical results are given in Figures 13, 14, 15 and 16. Figure 13 shows the distribution of throughput time for batches of work under the input and output conditions given in Figure 14. The work in progress generated by the average throughput time of approximately two weeks provided sufficient internal buffer stock to reduce the sharp fluctuations in weekly input to a much smaller fluctuation in output and labour utilization, shown in Figure 15. The stability of the

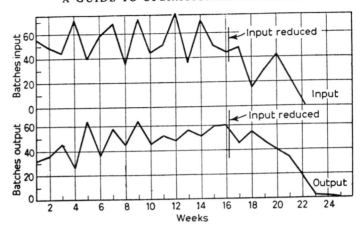

FIG. 14

Batches per week. Input and output.

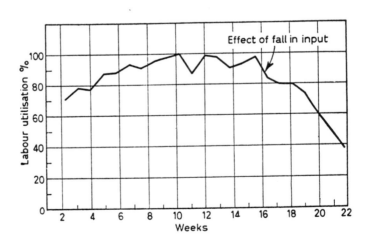

FIG. 15

Labour utilization (4½ week moving average).

throughput time is shown in Figure 16 in which the input and output are plotted on a cumulative basis. This is a very useful method of observing the condition of a factory unit because the horizontal

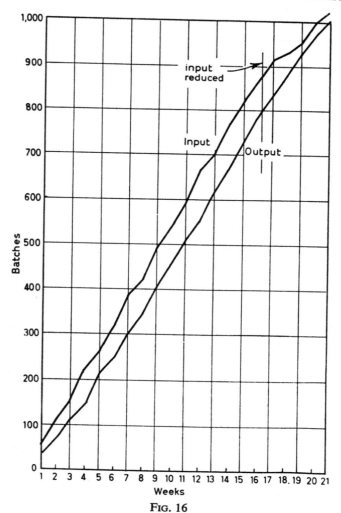

FIG. 16

Cumulative input and output of batches.

distance between the input and output lines at any stage gives the mean throughput time at that stage.

Where greater fluctuations in input than those shown in Figure 14 had to be tolerated the work in progress necessary to absorb these fluctuations and prevent excessive variation in labour utilization was readily calculable, as was the resulting increase in mean throughput time.

Electronic computer simulation of a complex production process is a very powerful O.R. tool for management. It enables the likely effects of many decisions to be estimated before they are taken so that harmful consequences are more likely to be avoided and beneficial combinations more likely to be observed.

A full report on simulation methods, which gives many practical examples of the technique and is written in an easily comprehended and readable manner, has been issued by Simulation Associates. A very good bibliography of the subject is included in the report.

Stock and production control models

Excessive stock has always been one of industry's main headaches. Many a managing director or plant manager must feel that if he could reduce his stocks he would have more money available for expanding his business and maybe more room to do it in.

There are really three problems to be considered. One is to decide what should be the minimum stock level of any component at which a fresh order for that component should be placed. The other two problems are to decide what amount to order when the order is placed, (a) when one is purchasing from an outside supplier, (b) when one is manufacturing the item oneself.

The problem of minimum safety stock or minimum re-order stock level, whatever one likes to call it, has been tackled in a variety of ways by O.R. workers. The problem arises because there is a delay between ordering the goods and receiving them and one needs a stock to cover sales during this delay. If sales were at a constant and predictable rate and delivery were assured in a certain time, then there would be no difficulty. The re-order stock level would be the exact amount of stock needed to provide for the quantity sold during the delivery period.

It is when both the sales rate and the delivery period vary that the difficulties become acute. If one allowed just enough stock to cover the average rate of sales during the average delivery period then it is not difficult to see that because about half of the sales rates would be above the average and about half of the delivery periods would also be above the average then in approximately 50 per cent of the cases the above amount of stock would not be sufficient and would be reduced to zero before the order arrived. Very few companies would tolerate such a high occurrence of delays in either providing customers with their demands or supplying other production departments with their requirements.

Thus stock in excess of what is required on the basis of average sales and average delivery times is carried. The smaller the risk of running out of stock the greater the stock that must be carried. Using the methods of mathematical statistics, it is possible, in any given situation, to calculate the size of stock to carry for given probabilities of running out of stock. When a manager is presented with a clear indication of what stock he must carry to reduce this risk to 1 in 500 or 1 in 1,000 (probabilities which many stock controllers feel they would like to achieve), he is often able to reconcile himself to a risk level of 1 in 50 in order to adjust his safety stock to a reasonably economic level. This risk level of 1 in 50 can often be more cheerfully accepted when calculations show that even when a 'stock out' occurs fresh supplies are available within a day or so.

In fact quite surprisingly high risks can sometimes be run if the period of delivery of the items is relatively short. It must be remembered also that the risks only apply to the items being ordered. If only a small proportion of items is on order at a given time, then the chance that any item is out of stock when a customer calls for it is very much less than the risk of a run out on the items being ordered. The following figures illustrate this. In a warehouse providing some 2,000 items ex stock, fresh supplies of each item were ordered from the suppliers on average every ten months. At any time some 30 per cent of the items would be on order, delivery being about three months. As a result of an O.R. study Table 4 was drawn up. This showed that the warehouse manager could operate a buffer stock policy which allowed 15 per cent of the items on order to run out of stock before being replenished, while running only a 2 per cent chance of

TABLE 4

Level of buffer stock in terms of average monthly sales	Percentage of ordered items expected to be out of stock before delivery is obtained	Percentage of items out of stock at any given time	Average time for these items to be out of stock
One month	26·4	3·5	0·8 months
Two months	14·7	2·0	0·7 months
Three months	8·9	1·2	0·6 months

offending a customer by not being able to supply immediately from stock.

The statistical methods used to evaluate the level of stock needed to provide a given level of protection need not be very complicated. The secretary of a small company once asked me to look at the purchasing policy of a branch office. This office was selling goods retail which it purchased wholesale. Despite the fact that the wholesaler was prepared to deliver weekly and offered no discount for quantity, the branch office purchased goods in substantial quantities at somewhat infrequent intervals. Its operations on a particular product for the first half of a given year are shown in Table 5.

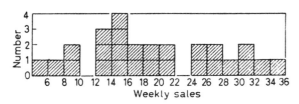

FIG. 17

Frequency distribution of weekly sales.

Figure 17 is a frequency distribution of the weekly sales for the first half of the year. There was no seasonal bias in the sales of this product therefore one could expect this same distribution to be approximately followed in the second half of the year. The chance of a weekly sale

TABLE 5

Week	Stock at end of week	Purchases during week	Sales during week
1	63	60	28
2	34	–	29
3	67	60	27
4	51	–	16
5	29	–	21
6	72	60	17
7	39	–	33
8	80	60	19
9	48	–	32
10	66	40	22
11	30	–	36
12	50	40	20
13	35	–	15
14	4	–	31
15	31	40	13
16	63	50	18
17	38	–	25
18	23	–	15
19	48	40	15
20	34	–	14
21	21	–	13
22	6	10	25
23	Nil	–	6
24	21	30	9
25	11	–	10
26	23	20	8

exceeding a given figure, say 40, can be mathematically calculated but for the purpose of simplicity it was assumed that no weekly sale would exceed 36 in the second half of the year. The risk of making this assumption is, of course, approximately 1 in 26, because in only one week out of the preceeding 26 had a sale as high as 36 been realized.

Thus it was merely necessary to ensure that the wholesaler delivered

TABLE 6

Week	Stock at end of week	Purchases during week	Sales during week
27	26	13	10
28	20	10	16
29	19	16	17
30	25	17	11
31	25	11	11
32	28	11	8
33	13	8	23
34	28	23	8
35	20	8	16
36	22	16	14
37	4	14	32
38	17	32	19
39	28	19	8
40	23	8	13
41	13	13	23
42	24	23	12
43	13	12	23
44	19	23	17
45	16	17	20
46	19	20	17
47	23	17	13
48	8	13	28
49	15	28	21
50	20	21	16
51	10	16	26
52	18	26	18

weekly and to order just the amount necessary to bring the stock at the beginning of each week up to 36. This would provide enough stock to meet all but exceptional sales in a week and because delivery from the wholesaler was so short the consequences of any 'stock out' would not be serious.

The effects of trying this simple rule on the second half of the year in question can be seen in Table 6. It can readily be seen that the rule of starting each week with a stock of 36 means that the week's order on the wholesaler equals the previous week's sales. This illustrates the simplicity of some of the rules which emerge from an O.R. study.

The actual behaviour of the branch office during the second half of the year (which was before the investigation was made) is given in Table 7.

TABLE 7

Week	Stock at end of week	Purchases during week	Sales during week
27	33	20	10
28	17	–	16
29	20	20	17
30	9	–	11
31	18	20	11
32	30	20	8
33	7	–	23
34	19	20	8
35	23	20	16
36	29	20	14
37	37	40	32
38	18	–	19
39	20	10	8
40	37	30	13
41	14	–	23
42	42	40	12
43	19	–	23
44	22	20	17
45	42	40	20
46	25	–	17
47	52	40	13
48	24	–	28
49	3	–	21
50	27	40	16
51	51	50	26
52	33	–	18

There were no 'stock outs' under either system, but the average weekly stock which would have been carried under the O.R. scheme of Table 6 was 19, that actually carried in Table 7 was 26. There was thus a saving of 27 per cent to be made in stock level by taking a known risk of a 'stock out'. A similar study in a company stocking steel products has been reported by Collcutt and his colleagues.

This rationalization of stock levels with commercial risks is usually the first task of an O.R. worker in investigating stock problems, and the savings which can accrue are often quite substantial. A further advantage is that when 'stock outs' occur in such a system, provided that they happen with the appropriate frequency, they are recognized as one of the expected consequences of the original management decision on stock levels. They do not become an opportunity to shower recriminations on the stock controller who, in the absence of such awareness, would seek protection in ever-increasing stocks.

Although emphasis has been placed so far on the determination of re-order stock level, the above considerations apply equally well to systems with a given re-order interval. Such systems have advantages in the ordering of components for assembly and have been discussed by Magee.

The second and third problems, those of re-order quantities are tackled in a somewhat different way. Again, two opposing commercial considerations are weighed against each other but this time probability does not enter into the calculation. The inherent variability of the system has already been taken care of in the chosen value of minimum stock level (re-order interval if the latter is used). The two considerations are, first the fact that one usually obtains the parts at a decreasing cost per item as the order size increases (this did not happen with the above example, hence the problem did not arise) and secondly the fact that the greater the order size the longer the parts remain in stock before being sold and hence the greater the storage and investment cost per item.

These two factors, the one decreasing the item cost, the other increasing it, can be represented graphically as follows:

Curve AA' is the curve showing how unit cost decreases with order quantity. The straight line BB' shows how unit storage and investment cost increases with order quantity, because, at a given rate of sale, the items remain in store for a longer period and thus take up space and require capital for a longer period. The dotted curve CC' is the sum of AA' and BB' and represents the change in the total cost per item with order quantity. It is seen that there is a minimum total cost per item at order quantity D and this, in simple situations, is the quantity which should be ordered.

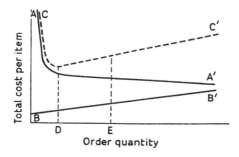

FIG. 18

This can be calculated in the following manner (non-mathematical readers may like to skip immediately to the formula at the end):

Let the fixed cost per order be c and the variable cost be m. Then the equation of line AA' is:

$$\text{Manufacturing cost per item} = \frac{c}{\text{Order quantity}} + m.$$

Let P be the interest and storage costs of the invested stock in per cent per month. In certain cases these can be calculated, in other cases, as explained later they can, for the purposes of control, be any figure considered appropriate in the circumstances. This figure need not necessarily be the Bank Rate or Dividend Rate or Expected Return on Invested Capital or any of the usual criteria.

Also let S be the average monthly sales rate of the item ordered. The average time for which an item is in stock will therefore be

$$\frac{1}{2}\left(\frac{\text{Order quantity}}{S}\right).$$

The interest which will be charged to the item for this period of time will be

$$\text{Manufacturing cost per item} \times \frac{\text{Order quantity}}{2S} \times \frac{P}{100}.$$

Hence the equation for line BB', is

Investment cost per item

$$= \left(\frac{c}{\text{Order quantity}} + m\right) \times \frac{\text{Order quantity}}{2S} \times \frac{P}{100}.$$

If we let the order quantity (whose value for minimum cost we want to find) be x, then the equation of the line CC' is

$$\text{Total cost per item} = \frac{c}{x} + m + \left(\frac{c}{x} + m\right)\frac{x}{2S}.\frac{P}{100}$$

$$= \frac{c}{x} + m + \frac{cP}{200S} + \frac{mP.x}{200S}.$$

The minimum value of this total cost per item, the point D, can be found mathematically, by differential calculus, to be where

$$x^2 = \frac{200cS}{n.P}$$

or

$$x = \sqrt{(200cS/mP)}.$$

This is the well-known square-root formula and it, and its derivatives, are bandied about by O.R. workers to a dangerous extent. It is safe to say that almost any ordering scheme which uses this formula will cause serious production difficulties in circumstances which will be discussed later, and will almost certainly result in an inflated level of stock being carried.

The economic justification for using the square-root formula is that by minimizing costs it maximizes profit. This justification needs closer examination. At first sight it seems appropriate because maximum profit is made from investments when the marginal return on capital is equal to the marginal cost of capital, and as shown below this equation gives the same square-root formula as before (again, non-mathematical readers may like to miss this proof):

$$\text{Cost per unit} = \frac{c}{x} + m$$

$$\text{Cost per batch} = c + mx$$

$$\text{Average capital investment} = \frac{c + mx}{2}$$

Let V = selling price, then

$$\text{Gross profit per unit} = V - \left(\frac{c}{x} + m\right)$$

$$\text{Gross profit per annum} = S\left[V - \left(\frac{c}{x} + m\right)\right]$$

$$\text{Rate of change of profit with quantity} = \frac{\partial\,\text{Profit}}{\partial x}$$

$$= \frac{Sc}{x^2}$$

$$\text{Rate of change of capital with quantity} = \frac{\partial\,\text{Capital}}{\partial x}$$

$$= \frac{m}{2}$$

Therefore

$$\frac{\partial\,\text{Profit}}{\partial\,\text{Capital}} = \text{Marginal rate of return on capital}$$

$$= \left(\frac{Sc}{x^2}\right)\Big/\left(\frac{m}{2}\right) = \frac{2Sc}{mx^2}$$

To maximize profits

$$\text{Marginal return on capital} = \text{Marginal cost of capital}$$

$$= P/100$$

Therefore

$$\frac{2Sc}{mx^2} = P/100$$

$$x = \sqrt{\left(\frac{200cS}{mP}\right)} \quad \text{(as before).}$$

If the shape of the curve of marginal rate of return on capital, as shown in Figure 19, is examined however, it is seen to fall sharply with increase of batch size and then decline only slowly until it eventually crosses the line.

$$\text{Marginal cost of capital} = P$$

at batch size D.

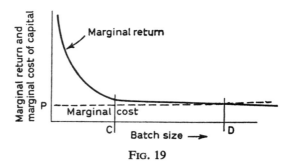

FIG. 19

The full line is the marginal return and the dotted line is the marginal cost line.

Over the range of batch size CD the marginal return on capital is very little greater than the marginal cost of capital and while this would not matter to a firm with unlimited capital, to a company with only a limited amount of capital, and most firms are in this situation, serious consideration should be given as to whether further investment beyond C would not better be made in some other product where the marginal return on the capital invested would be higher than in the region CD.

The very small advantage gained to the company by increasing its batch sizes beyond C (say, half the quantity predicted by the square-root formula) can be shown in the following example, which can once more be missed by non-mathematicians:

let

$$S = 100 \text{ per annum}$$

$$m = £2$$

$$c = £10$$

$$P = 10 \text{ per cent}$$

$$V = £4$$

then

$$x = \sqrt{\left(\frac{200 \times 10 \times 100}{2 \times 10}\right)} = 100.$$

The net annual profit is

Average investment × (Average return on capital −

Average cost of capital).

$$\text{Average investment} = \frac{£(10+2x)}{2} = £(5+x).$$

Average rate of return on capital

$$= \frac{£S\left(V - \left[\frac{c}{x} + m\right]\right)}{\dfrac{c + mx}{2}} = £200\left(\frac{4}{10+2x} - \frac{1}{x}\right)$$

$$= \frac{400}{5+x} - \frac{200}{x}.$$

$$\text{Average cost of capital} = 10 \text{ per cent} = \frac{10}{100}.$$

$$\text{Net annual profit} = £(5+x)\left(\frac{400}{5+x} - \frac{200}{x} - \frac{1}{10}\right)$$

$$= £400 - \frac{200(5+x)}{x} - \frac{5+x}{10}$$

$$= £100\left(4 - 2 - \frac{1}{200} - \frac{10}{x} - \frac{x}{1000}\right)$$

63

With batch size $x = 100$

Average investment $= £105$

Net annual profit $= £179 \cdot 5$

With batch size $\dfrac{x}{2} = 50$

Average investment $\quad = £55$

Net annual profit $\quad = £174 \cdot 5$.

Thus by using a batch size of x in place of a batch size of $x/2$, the capital employed is about doubled with a resulting increase in annual profit of only 3 per cent. Most boards of directors could do better than this by doubling the amount of capital employed in their business.

The reason for this meagre result is that with a batch size of $x/2$ £55 of capital earn a marginal rate of return of

$$\frac{1000}{x^2} = \frac{1000}{2500} = 40 \text{ per cent}$$

whereas, with a batch size of x the £105 of capital employed only earn a marginal rate of return of

$$\frac{1000}{10,000} = 10 \text{ per cent}$$

(as is to be expected since this equals the marginal cost of capital of 10 per cent).

If there are other ways within the firm where a marginal rate of return greater than 10 per cent can be earned, then the batch size should be reduced below x so as to free capital for this use.

Thus an uninformed use of the square-root formula can lead to batch sizes, and hence stocks, in excess of those which are in the true interest of the firm.

There are many other reasons why the square-root formula should not be used for fixing batch sizes. Many of the assumptions about set-up charges, etc., underlying its construction just do not apply in practice. This has been forcefully pointed out by Burbidge.

When used to determine batch sizes in a factory, the square-root formula leads to production difficulties as pointed out by Salveson. Using this formula each item is ordered on the factory in proportion to the square root of its own sales rate. However, each product will continue to be sold in direct proportion to its own sales rate. There will thus be a lack of balance between the order quantities of these different products and their rates of sale. This will not matter if the several articles represent only a small proportion of the plant's output, because then they will not get in each other's way. But if they do account for the bulk of the plant capacity then there will be occasions when two separate articles will need to be produced at the same time. This is impossible, of course, and the makeshift which will have to be

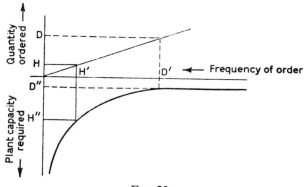

FIG. 20

D″ is plant capacity required for order quantity D at frequency D′. H″ is plant capacity required for order quantity H at frequency H′.

introduced will cause departure from what was considered to be an optimum policy.

Plant capacity is of importance too in deciding upon the optimum amount to order. The smaller the quantities the less the investment in stock, but the greater the proportion of unproductive time spent in setting up and the more frequently the orders have to be placed. Figure 20 shows that the plant capacity may not be sufficient to allow the order quantity to become too small.

The final choice, as in all such cases, is up to management.

This illustrates what was said in the Introduction, that it is not the object of O.R. to usurp the decision-making function of a manager, it is to give it a greater scientific precision, a cutting edge. Thus instead of worrying which value to place on investment interest or chivvying accountants to provide it, the O.R. worker calculates several schemes based on different values of investment interest, etc., and presents these to the manager, who has to make the decision.

This manager has his own intuitive assessment of the level of investment which the company can carry and of the production cycle lengths which are economically acceptable. This assessment is based upon a whole host of intangible factors which no O.R. investigation can hope to tease out. The assessment will vary according to the economy not only of the firm in question but also of the country as a whole. When this assessment can be used to select one from a variety of schemes which the O.R. man presents, and each of which is internally consistent then the most fruitful and effective combination of intuitive and scientific insight has resulted. The manager knows at what level he wants his company or departments to operate. The O.R. man can ensure that it operates at that level consistently and most people familiar with existing stock and production control schemes know that the bugbear is their inconsistency. Stocks of one part can be sky-rocketing, while panic measures are resorted to for obtaining enough supplies of another part.

An O.R. scheme of stock control can in fact give a manager 'Finger tip' control of his stock and production system. Consider, for example, a simple order system in which the ordered quantity is best related directly to the sales rate of each product. Then all the manager has to do is to find the value of K in the equation.

$$\text{Order quantity} = KS$$

where S is the monthly rate of sales of the items in question.

To do this he need know nothing of set-up costs or manufacturing costs or investment rates. He just sets K. After a time he may learn that stocks are high, or that the factories are having to set-up too often for too small quantities or that run-outs are frequent because of too frequent ordering. To correct the situation he merely alters the value of K. He will know that when everything is running smoothly and factories, sales department and accountants are equally satisfied (or dissatisfied) that he has chosen the right value. To aid him initially he could of course have a simulation carried out and choose the value of

K which optimizes results in the simulation. The point is that once a scheme has been chosen which ensures consistency of ordering throughout the system the parameters can be set by the controlling

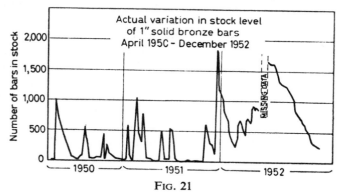

FIG. 21

Before O.R. investigation.

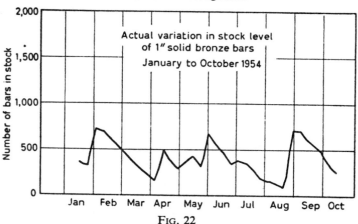

FIG. 22

After O.R. scheme.

manager without the need for detailed cost or production studies and these parameters can be changed at will to meet changing situations.

The results of giving a manager some quite simple schemes can often be very encouraging as seen in Figures 21 and 22, which illustrate the effect on one stock control system of the initiation of a simple O.R. plan whose level of operation was left to the manager concerned.

One precaution which must be observed when simple stock control schemes, such as the ones described, are inaugurated is that the effect of a change in the system should be examined. For example, the scheme in which items are re-ordered when a certain level of buffer stock is reached, and the order quantity is proportional to the sales rate, is subject to the acceleration effect. When sales increase steadily over a long period the buffer stock is reached more frequently and the order quantity increases each time an order is placed. The combined effect of these two changes is to increase the total orders placed by more than the increase in sales. In fact as sales increase the order volume is increased by the square of the increase in sales. When sales decline over a long period, the opposite effect occurs. The result is illustrated in Figure 23.

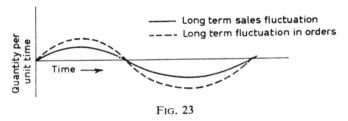

Fig. 23

Although this 'acceleration' of orders relative to sales may seem undesirable, especially if the goods are produced in the same organization which sells them and it may therefore lead to overstrained resources, it is really the correct policy to pursue. This is because orders must always be placed in advance of sales and if sales are continually increasing then the orders must be increasing at a faster rate in order that the goods will be in stock when required. This 'out of phase' effect is illustrated in Figure 24.

The orders graph and sales graph are assumed identical in shape, as they should be if the order policy in sensible, but because the orders graph must be displaced ahead of the sales graph, i.e. earlier in time, its gradient at a given point of time (say t), that is, the rate of increase of orders with time, must be higher than that of the sales graph at the same time.

68

Thus if a factory expects its sales to increase at an accelerating rate over a long period it must be prepared to produce goods at an even faster rate of increase if its delivery periods are not to lengthen. If it expects its sales to fluctuate over long periods of time as shown in Figure 23, then either it must be prepared for fluctuations in its work load of an even greater magnitude or it must carry a strategic buffer stock to enable it to sell at a higher rate than it is producing for as long as the increase in sales permits. This stock can be replenished during the period of low sales.

This strategic stock is kept for different reasons than the tactical buffer stock which enables random fluctuations in sales to be coped with.

This example illustrates the use of operational research thinking in both strategic and tactical spheres.

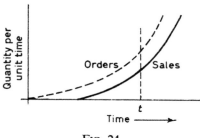

FIG. 24

The 'acceleration' effect is a well-known effect in industry and can cause a minor boom in sales at one end of a productive chain to be experienced as a major boom at the other end. Contrariwise, a minor drop in sales can cause a serious recession. The solution depends on a full understanding of the causes of the acceleration and co-operation between all links in the productive chain in keeping either adequate stocks or adequate reserve of capacity. The problem has been very fully discussed by Forrester.

When the optimum order quantities have been decided problems may occur in scheduling these through the factories in the optimum manner. If the products form the bulk of a factory's or department's output, then quite complex methods of the linear programming or queueing theory type may be needed, or a comprehensive simulation may have to be used. Even in simple situations the problems may be difficult to solve. With nine products, for example, being made in one process there are more than 360,000 ways in which the order of manufacture can be arranged. Clearly it is impossible for any scheduling officer to consider all the combinations, and thus he cannot be sure he has the optimum arrangement.

Operational Research is finding solutions to these problems, however, and even when scheduling seems simple it is worth while carrying out an investigation.

Consider the nine products below which require manufacture on two machines A and B successively for the times given in Table 8. What is the order in which to do the jobs which will minimize the total time, bearing in mind that a job cannot transfer to machine B until it has finished on machine A?

TABLE 8

	Time on Machine	
Product	A	B
1	4	2
2	5	3
3	5	4
4	3	9
5	2	1
6	5	7
7	2	4
8	2	6
9	7	5

Figure 25 shows that the order given in Table 8 is very wasteful of time because machine B is left waiting very often for a job to finish on machine A. The simple rule which Johnson has devised to deal with this situation is as follows: Find the smallest machining time. If this is on Machine B, put the job in question at the end, if it is on machine A, put it at the beginning. Then find the next smallest machining time and proceed in the same way by making the job concerned either the second or the second last. Where several jobs have the same smallest

70

time rank them in order of the associated time on the other machine. In the case of Table 8 this will lead to the following schedule:

TABLE 9

	Time on Machine	
Job No.	A	B
7	2	4
8	2	6
4	3	9
6	5	7
9	7	5
3	5	4
2	5	3
1	4	2
5	2	1

This schedule, as shown in Figure 26, takes less total time than the original schedule of Table 8 and Figure 25.

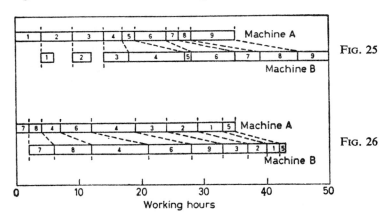

FIGS. 25 & 26
Scheduling of nine jobs on two machines.

With this kind of elementary rule O.R. can often assist in scheduling even the simplest kind of production situation. This rule of Johnson's can be extended, with difficulty, to more than two machines, but it is not applicable for continuous scheduling, i.e. where jobs are continually coming into the shop because then a product with a small machining time on the second machine might be put back indefinitely. Operational Research workers are searching for other rules to use in continuous scheduling problems. Complex scheduling problems of quite a different type are considered under Network Analysis on page 99.

Decision theory

The art of decision-making is a very complicated one and it is in essence the true art of management. In industry one is paid for making decisions so it is natural that O.R. workers should study the process and assess how it may be improved. Three techniques are being examined, decision theory, game theory and operational gaming.

The decision theory approach has been described in some detail by Good. In his Principle of Rational Decisions the decision-maker tries to maximize expected utility, where:

Expected Utility

= Probability of Success × Value of Success

− Probability of Failure × Cost of Failure

An illustration of this principle is the tossing of pennies for reward. Suppose one is playing a game with an opponent. If the penny comes down heads, he pays you a penny, if tails, you pay him. In this game

$$\text{Probability of Success} = \tfrac{1}{2}$$
$$\text{Value of Success} = 1d.$$
$$\text{Probability of Failure} = \tfrac{1}{2}$$
$$\text{Cost of Failure} = 1d.$$

Therefore

$$\text{Expected Utility} = \tfrac{1}{2} \times 1d. - \tfrac{1}{2} \times 1d. = 0.$$

One would not expect to gain or lose much from joining such a game and one certainly would not do so with any expectation of profit. This result is in accord with experience.

Another illustration is the football pool situation. The probability of winning £75,000 on the eight results with a single stake is about

1/73,000,000. The stake, which one loses anyway, is 1s. Therefore
Expected Utility = (1/73,000,000 × £75,000) − 1s.

This is very nearly equal to − 1s. and is in accordance with the
common knowledge that one expects to lose one's first stake in a
football pool.

A more general treatment of the football pool case along the lines
indicated above would show that the Expected Utility is always
negative and is cumulatively so for a man's lifetime. This is not
invalidated by the fact that some people win, because this situation is a
closed one, i.e. a certain amount of money *must* be won. For the great
majority of people, however, the Utility, as well as the Expected Utility
is negative.

Where one is comparing two situations and deciding whether to
choose between them the Expected Utility is maximized, and the actual
value may not be important. For instance, if one is compelled to
gamble, the tossing pennies situation is more attractive than the football pool one because although the Expected Utility for tossing
pennies is zero, it is nevertheless greater than that for football pools.
This may explain why most people do not mind mild gambling when
playing cards, although they would refuse to join a football pool
syndicate. Social pressure plays a part here of course, but even so the
comparison is probably valid. Professional gamblers certainly do not
make their living from football pools but gamble in situations ana-
logous to the tossing pennies game. They usually contrive to sway the
odds in their favour so that the Expected Utility is positive.

It therefore seems that this principle gives results in accordance
with reality. There is one class of exceptions however. If one had to
send £5 by post one would be faced with the decision whether or not to
register this amount. A decision to register would prevent a loss of
£5. However, the Expected Utility is as follows:

$$\text{Expected Utility} = \left(\frac{1}{50,000} \times £5\right) - 1s.$$

where $\frac{1}{50,000}$ is the G.P.O. figure for the proportion of lost registered
letters and 1s. is the cost of registration. This Expected Utility is
negative, yet in many cases one decides to register. Why?

The reason is that a certain delay ensues between posting the £5 and
hearing that it has arrived safely. During this time one may be anxious

about the fate of the money. Registration provides a way out of the anxiety, so in effect one ascribes a value to one's 'peace of mind' and turns the Expected Utility from negative to positive by so doing.

Another interpretation of the decision to register is the application of the minimax principle, which will be discussed later.

The use of the Principle of Rational Decisions in a given situation therefore requires the evaluation of the probabilities of certain events and the values and costs associated with them together with assessment of such factors as peace of mind. This is not an easy matter of course and very few decisions in industry have been taken as a result of calculating the Expected Utility. Nevertheless the exercise is a useful one because it sharpens the executive's perception of the risks he may be running in preferring certain choices and the consequences he may have to face if those choices are the wrong ones.

The design of a new plant to manufacture an existing product was under consideration. The existing plant, although adequate in terms of output and quality was thought to be more costly to operate than a new one, which could be designed. The decision which had to be made was whether or not to proceed with the design of a new plant.

The decision clearly would not be a once for all matter like deciding on the spin of a coin. If the project were started and proved a failure it could be stopped. If the project were a success the benefits of the correct decision would be reaped for many years. To take account of the temporal factors the Expected Utility was calculated as follows:

Expected Utility for 1st year

> = Probability of Success in 1st year
> × Value of Success in 1st year
> − Probability of Failure in 1st year
> × Cost of Failure in 1st year.

Expected Utility for 2nd year

> = Probability of Success in 2nd year
> × Value of Success in 2nd year
> − Probability of Failure in 2nd year
> × Cost of Failure in 2nd year.

By plotting the Expected Utility against time the rapidity with which it became positive could be ascertained and thus the correctness of the decision assessed.

The relationship between probability of success and time was evolved after much research into the time taken for similar projects to be completed and the resulting curve is shown in Figure 27. The probability of a successful design of plant is the ordinate and the number of man-months of design staff time needed is the abscissa.

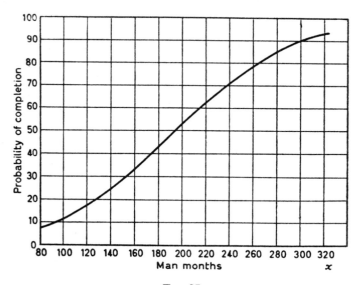

FIG. 27

Probability of completion of design within x man-months.

This curve enabled the probabilities of success and of failure (1 − Probability of Success) to be calculated each year with given numbers of design staff working on the project. The values of success and failure were obtained with the help of financial staff and the resulting decision functions constructed for various selected circumstances.

None of the results was sufficiently encouraging to justify much optimism in the project and for this and other reasons, such as more promising alternative uses of resources, the project was abandoned.

It is always difficult to assess whether or not a decision *not* to do something has been correct, but it was fairly clear some years after that the decision taken was the right one.

The negative decision not to proceed was taken because the forecast for the Expected Utility of the project each year into the future was not sufficiently encouraging. If the positive decision to proceed with the project had been taken then the real utility of the project could have been checked against the original forecast and a revised forecast each year and the wisdom of proceeding with the project could have been assessed.

Many other rules have been postulated by mathematicians for making choices in decision situations and experience suggests that one commonly used, albeit intuitively, by managers is the 'minimax' principle. This is illustrated below:

| | *Outcome* | | | |
Choice	A	B	C	D
1	− 500	+ 300	+ 600	− 800
2	+ 400	+ 200	− 100	− 300
3	− 600	− 900	+ 200	+ 500
4	− 500	+ 400	+ 700	− 200

Nos. 1, 2, 3 and 4 are four choices placed before a manager; A, B, C and D are four possible outcomes which may occur once a choice has been made. The negative numbers indicate the losses which may arise from each choice in the event of a certain outcome. Thus if choice 3 is made and the outcome is B, then a maximum loss of 900 could occur. Some of the values are positive, indicating that with the particular combination of events a profit would be made.

What choice would you make: 1, 2, 3 or 4? The minimax rule says choice 2, because then the maximum loss 300 in the worst outcome D is lower than the maximum loss in the worst outcome with any other choice, whose maximum losses are respectively 800, 900 and 500. Thus by choosing 2 one has minimized one's maximum loss – hence the term 'minimax'.

You may prefer other rules. You may prefer choice 4 because it gives the highest average profit. In practice, however, it is found that managers tend to be pessimistic in their judgements and to safeguard themselves and their companies' assets by choosing the alternatives which lose least if they go wrong, rather than profit most if they go right. This has been demonstrated by Mills. To be aware of this and also to assess the probabilities of the various outcomes, which have been excluded from the table opposite for the sake of simplicity, can often be a valuable exercise and can aid the executive in reaching an appropriate decision.

For example, as stated earlier, the decision to register a letter can be seen as an application of the minimax rule. The matrix of choices and outcomes is shown below, with the loss at each combination inserted in the appropriate place.

	Outcome	
Choice	*Letter lost*	*Letter not lost*
Register	$-1s.$	$-1s.$
Do not register	$-£5$	0

The choice which minimizes the maximum loss is clearly to register. This is a safety-first policy and in operating it we should be quite clear that we are paying $1s.$ for the privilege of doing so. In industrial situations the cost of using the minimax principle may be very high and the formulation of the decision in the above form helps us to recognize this. This illustrates one purpose of O.R. which is to make explicit things which have hitherto been implicit and therefore have been less easily recognized and changed when necessary.

In the above situation, for instance, a firm which was sending out many valuable letters might well decide not to register them because observation over a long period would produce the result that the cost of registering was in excess of the amount recovered. This brings us back to the utility formulation of the problem and it may well be that a consistent application of the minimax rule would result ultimately in far greater losses than the taking of occasional risks.

To sum up, therefore, it might be said that if you are faced occasionally with decisions whose outcome could result in substantial losses then the minimax rule is a good one to apply, but that if you have a succession of such decisions to take then a maximization of the expected utility is appropriate.

This choice of decision criterion can be illustrated with reference to a hoary subject of controversy in industry, preventive maintenance. In one company a large plant was known to be deteriorating. The choice facing the manager was between *ad hoc* maintenance and radical re-equipping. The cost of the *ad hoc* maintenance was £500, that of re-equipping £3,000. A factory holiday was approaching during which the re-equipping could be done. Another such opportunity would not occur for a year. Should the *ad hoc* maintenance fail, therefore, and the re-equipping have to be carried out eventually, a severe loss of production might result, costing £70,000. The possibility of this occurring was estimated as 1 : 100.

The utility expressions were therefore as follows:

$$\text{Expected Utility of } ad hoc \text{ maintenance } = -£500 - \frac{1}{100} \times 70,000$$

$$= -£1,200$$

$$\text{Expected Utility of re-equipping } = -£3,000$$

Maximization of Expected Utility therefore suggested deciding for *ad hoc* maintenance, since this had the smaller negative value. The matrix of choices and outcomes was, however, as follows:

Choice	Outcome	
	Maintenance succeeds	*Maintenance fails*
Ad hoc maintenance	− 500	− 70,000
Re-equipping	− 3,000	− 3,000

The minimax rule suggests re-equipping. In this case because it was a once-for-all decision, and because although the chance of the maintenance failing was small its consequence was so serious, the minimax rule was followed and the plant re-equipped during the shut-down.

In the same factory, however, many machines are operated until they break down, because the probability of breakdown is such that only a few machines are out of action at a time, and thus the utility is maximized by not carrying out preventive maintenance. This is an illustration of how in situations where probability has a real interpretation in terms of frequency it is better to maximize the expected utility than to use the minimax principle.

The minimax principle can of course be applied in situations where the outcomes of the various alternative choices cannot be expressed quantitatively, or where it is difficult to do so. Consider the perennial choice which faces all of us in a typical English summer, 'Shall I carry a mac or umbrella or not?'

Here the minimax rule is applied by saying to oneself, 'Which decision shall I regret more if it is the wrong one?' If you would regret carrying an umbrella or mac around, if it is a fine day, more than being caught in the rain without either if it turns out wet, then you will not take any protection. If you would regret more being caught in the rain, then you take an umbrella.

Clearly the choice depends on circumstances. If you ride around in a car and at worst would only have a short dash in a shower of rain, the preference may be not to take the mac. If you would be seriously inconvenienced in rain, then you protect yourself.

The choice also depends upon probabilities. If the sky in the morning appears overcast, the decision will be weighted in favour of the mac. If the sky has been cloudless for days, only a pessimist would bother. Thus these decision functions can be applied even in qualitative situations.

It is important for a managing director to appreciate that the minimax rule is probably being intuitively applied by many of his staff in making their day-to-day decisions. In the lower strata of the executive structure, safety first is a much more powerful watchword than the maximization of Expected Utility which may, as shown above, be far more advantageous to the company where repetitive judgements are required. Stock control is the prime example of the minimax attitude. It may benefit the company financially to allow 5 per cent of its products to be out of stock, but this decision an individual stock controller often dare not make. It should, very properly, be made by the managing director, who, aware of the damaging effect that the minimax rule may have in such situations, should see to it that the appropriate rule for maximization of Expected Utility is teased out and applied.

The purpose of operational research is, after all, to help managers to take decisions and, if possible, to help them to take fewer decisions.

Now decision taking is an energy consuming task. We all know the story of the Civil Servant working happily in a friends' orchard picking apples who broke down after being asked to sort the apples while he picked them. 'All those decisions' killed him. Yet too few managers take this to heart in their working life. Too few seek ways of reducing the number of decisions they need to take. Too few welcome the activities of others who wish to ease their burdens and free them for higher levels of responsibility.

Mention was made at the top of page 16 of the further study made by the O.R. department in a jobbing firm into the estimating system used. This further analysis showed that a great deal of unnecessary work was being done and a great many decisions were being required of both estimating and sales staff of a continually recurring type and which took skills and energy which could more properly be diverted to other purposes.

Many of the products being estimated could, for example, be manufactured in a variety of ways. The estimators felt constrained to decide at the time of estimating upon the method of manufacture which would be used if and when the order for the parts was received. To carry out this responsibility they sought information from the factories about the current and future utilization of the various manufacturing techniques and incorporated this knowledge into their choice of estimating technique. Other considerations, such as quantity of parts required, also influenced their decisions and made the whole procedure of estimating a very complex task requiring a good deal of engineering skill, knowledge of factory procedure, etc.

Even the process of calculating the material content of the part to be manufactured called for a high degree of ability. In the case of parts to be blanked out of steel strip, for example, the width of steel strip to be purchased was determined from a table of available standard widths. The estimator then had to decide whether the part could best be produced by blanking along or across the strip. He also had to determine whether tooling existed; if it could readily be manufactured; or if existing parts could be 'cannibalized'. He then had to calculate the amount of subsequent machining required, the value of the scrap salvaged, and so on.

Similar calculations were repeated for pressing costs, machining cost, electroplating costs where specified, etc. Possible losses due to the production of scrap had to be calculated and so the estimator had to have available information on rates of scrap of different processes. The whole procedure, it will be seen, was extremely complex for what were, in fact, relatively simple engineering shapes, although manufactured to a high precision. Many troublesome low-level decisions were also required by highly skilled staff.

Examination by the Operational Research Department of the results of these complex estimating procedures showed that very similar results could be obtained by using simple algebraic formulae. The material content, for instant, was quite simply related to the total value of the material required. As a result of this and similar exercises into manufacturing costs it became possible to devise a series of estimating formulae which could be operated by relatively unskilled staff, eliminating many of the decisions which were necessitated in the existing procedure.

Concurrently with the investigation into costing a study had been made into pricing procedure, led by the Managing Director who throughout took a leading and vigorous part in the whole exercise. It was found that when the Sales Managers received the estimates they were not able, as had originally been envisaged, to put on a percentage for 'profit' and then quote a price. When this was attempted strong reactions from customers often occurred. They had been quoted for similar parts previously which may have been estimated by a different estimator who had different ideas or different information about the techniques of manufacturer which would be used. Special prices may also have been negotiated at particular times because of prevailing market conditions. Customers sometimes quoted prices obtained from competitive firms who used quite different techniques, both for manufacture and for pricing.

It had long been realized by the Sales Organization, therefore, that any price structure based simply on the estimates would not be accepted by many customers and would result in much lost business. When the Sales Managers received the estimates they, too, were involved in numerous decisions and the seeking of information about previous quotations, etc., before being able to quote a price. Even so, because of the arbitrary nature of most of the decisions and the fact that they were made by different Sales Managers in different circumstances, the resulting price structure was far from consistent and still caused occasional strong reaction from customers and loss of business.

The Operational Research Department, therefore, carried out an analysis of the pricing structure in a similar way to its analysis of the estimating structure. The knowledge it had gained in examining the estimating structure was of course immensely useful. It was found that many of the simplifying formulae which had been developed in the estimating study could be applied in the development of a viable pricing structure because, being based upon the dimensions and features determined from a drawing known to a customer and not influenced directly by processes of manufacture not known to a customer, they had more reality from the customers' point of view than had the previous estimates.

The new system not only relieved the estimators and Sales Managers of a large number of *ad hoc* decisions which had previously been forced on them, it gave the Managing Director far greater control over pricing policy than he had had before. Attempts to increase the price of a particular class of products by raising the overhead allocated to that category had often resulted in changes in estimates on other products which had only caused confusion or even loss of income. Because prices were not strictly related to estimates the accounting system based upon estimates could not give the Managing Director any information on how successful he had been at increasing prices.

The Sales Managers, freed from their numerous *ad hoc* decisions, were able to concentrate on higher level decisions involving long term marketing problems and keeping a check on possible changes in the viability of the pricing formulae. The estimators were completely relieved of their estimating duties and were able to use their skills and knowledge to impose manufacturing procedures. The company now has a pricing department employing 5 people who produce twice as many prices as were formerly produced by 25 estimators together with a good deal of auxiliary work by the costing department. (Brown).

Game theory

Game theory is an extension of decision theory where, instead of one's choice of action being conditional on the possibilities of several outcomes, it is determined by the possible alternative actions of an opponent playing the same game.

In the kind of games considered both opponents take action simultaneously and are only aware of the other's reply after they have made their own choice. Many competitive situations in business are akin to this.

Consider the table below:

	A	B	C	D
α	4	2	4	3
β	2	−4	2	0
γ	3	−6	4	2
δ	4	−2	2	1

The choices α, β, γ, δ are the possible strategies, say of oneself, and A, B, C, D, are the possible strategies of one's opponent. How should one play the game? If one plays strategy β one gains 2 points if the opponent plays A or C, but loses 4 if he plays B. One cannot be sure when one plays β what choice one's opponent has made.

Here, again, a minimax rule exists. If one plays strategy α, one wins at least 2. If one plays any other strategy one might not win as much. If the opponent plays B, he does not lose more than 2. If he plays any other strategy he could lose more. Thus one's own minimum gain is the same as the opponent's maximum loss. The square αB is unique in this respect and this is called the saddle point or the solution of the game. When playing against a skilful opponent in this kind of situation one cannot do better in the long run than play this optimum strategy.

It is the merit of the game-theory approach that it has shown that all two-person games in which what one person wins the other loses have this kind of saddle point, although they are far more complex than in the above example. The solutions do not consist of a single strategy as above, but most often of a mixture of strategies, that is to say they involve the playing of choice α, say, 60 per cent of the time and choice β the remaining 40 per cent. The principle is the same however. In a given situation one can choose a mixture of strategies such that whatever the opponent does he cannot do better than a certain result which is calculable in advance. The advantage of this fore-knowledge in competitive situations is obvious.

For example take a simple finger game which is akin to Morra (described by Williams), but which is much easier to analyse. The game of Morra, which is many centuries old, is analysed fully in Williams's book and if you can learn the strategy he suggests, and can then persuade your friends to play with you for money, you may make quite a killing. The optimum strategy is far from obvious.

In our simple finger game the two players A and B agree to put up one or two fingers each simultaneously. If both players put up one finger or both put up two, then player A wins 2d. from B. If player A puts up one finger and B two fingers, then B wins 3d. from A. If A puts up two fingers and B one finger, then B wins 1d. from A.

What is the optimum strategy for each play?

To solve the game needs but a little arithmetic. First, we construct the table of the game as seen from A's point of view. This is called the pay-off matrix.

		B	
		1 finger	2 fingers
A	1 finger	2d.	$-3d$.
	2 fingers	$-1d$.	2d.

There is no straightforward minimax here because there is no single strategy by either player in which his minimum gain is the other's maximum loss. If B consistently puts up two fingers, hoping thereby to win 3d., A would then consistently put up two fingers and win 2d. If B then changed to one finger, to win at least 1d., A would then also change to one finger and again win 2d. If B then realized A was always putting up one finger he would put up two and win 3d. A would then change to two fingers and the whole cycle would repeat itself. There is thus no single choice of either side which forms a saddle point as in the previous example.

There is, however, by the theory of games, a mixture of strategies to which the game converges and at which there is a minimax solution. This mixture of strategies for player A can be found as follows.

Subtract the second column in the pay-off matrix from the first thus:

		Pay-off matrix B		Subtraction	Result
		1 finger	2 fingers		
A	1 finger	2	−3	2−(−3)	5
	2 fingers	−1	2	−1−2	−3

The correct mixture of strategies for A is to put up one finger three times to every five times he puts up two fingers. It would clearly be wrong to do this in order every time, because B would soon become aware of what was happening and would plan accordingly. A chooses the strategies in random order in such a manner that B has no means of knowing how many fingers are going up next, even though he may know that A is putting up one and two fingers in the ratio 3:5.

A good way for A to do this is to divide up the face of his watch into eight sections, allocate the first three to the one-finger play and the other five to the two-finger play. Then each time before he puts his finger up he just glances at his watch and decides his choice according to which section the second hand happens to be in. If it is in one of the first three sections he will put up one finger, if in one of the other five he puts up two fingers. In this way B cannot possibly know what A is going to do because A does not know himself until he glances at his watch!

The optimum choice of strategies for B is found in a similar way, this time by substracting the second row from the first one.

		B		
		1 finger	2 fingers	
A	1 finger	2	−3	Pay-off matrix
	2 fingers	−1	2	
		2−(−1)	−3−2	Substraction
		3	−5	Result

B chooses one finger 5 times and two fingers 3 times, again in a random fashion.

The minimax solution of the game is thus that A puts up one finger 3 times and two fingers 5 times, while B puts up one finger 5 times and two fingers 3 times. This is a minimax solution, because it can be shown that if A is playing his optimum mixed strategy, then B can do no better than play his own optimum mixed strategy.

This is illustrated in the following way. If A and B both play their optimum strategies the average pay-off to A is

$$= \tfrac{3}{8}\{\tfrac{5}{8}.2d. + \tfrac{3}{8}.(-3d.)\} + \tfrac{5}{8}\{\tfrac{5}{8}.(-1d.) + \tfrac{3}{8}.2d.)\}$$

$$= \tfrac{1}{8}d.$$

If B plays a pure strategy, say two fingers all the time, the pay-off to A, if A continues his mixed strategy is

$$\tfrac{3}{8}(-3d.) + \tfrac{5}{8}.2d. = \tfrac{1}{8}d.$$

Thus A still wins the same average amount. If B persisted in his two-finger strategy however A would then change to a two-finger strategy, and would win $2d$. continually. Therefore once A has decided on an optimum mixed strategy B can do no better than follow his own optimum mixed strategy, and thus the game has a mixed strategy saddle point. The reader can calculate for himself that if B plays his optimum strategy he still loses $\tfrac{1}{8}d$., but at least he loses no more than this! Methods of solution to more complicated games, and an explanation of the theory behind these methods, will be found in the book by Williams.

Once again, as in decision theory, the evaluation of all the components of games in real life is a difficult task, but it has been done with success in simple situations in some companies and the clarification it gives as to the correct choice of action is very illuminating.

The theory is in a very early stage of course, but with greater experience and more knowledge of how to evaluate the relevant parameters it can make a contribution to the manager's ability for decision-making.

Operational gaming

This should not be confused with game theory which, as shown in the previous chapter, is a mathematical method of obtaining solutions to competitive situations. Operational gaming is akin to simulation, but instead of dealing with a purely mechanistic situation, such as the operation of a machine shop or the behaviour of a stock control system, the human element in decision-making is brought in and studied.

The games (or business models as they are better called) are designed to imitate competitive situations in industry and to observe the performance of the men who take the roles of managing director, sales manager, production manager and so on in the imaginary companies which are set up. The models can also help in evolving the most successful policies in the competitive situations simulated.

Two major classes of these 'business models' are in existence. In both models the managers of each company have to allocate their cash resources each 'quarter of a year' between the following requirements – production; sales, advertising, and market research; research and development; and plant capacity. In addition they have to decide the price of their product (in the games all companies are manufacturing the same single product). One of the models, developed by the American Management Association, is designed to simulate a consumer goods industry and the other, developed by the American consulting firm of McKinsey, a capital goods industry.

With the A.M.A. model all decisions are made in financial terms and mathematical equations are used to determine the outcome of the decisions which result from external circumstances unknown to the players and from the interaction of the decisions of the various companies. For example, in the modification played in the Glacier Metal Co., the total market at any time is determined by a trend laid down before the start of play, which is influenced by the total marketing and research expenditure of the fictitious companies involved and by their combined price policy. Each company's own share of this market is determined by the relationship of its own marketing, research expenditure and price to that of the other companies.

Thus although the model might be said to be determined in the sense that the combined effect of all the companies' decisions is determined by mathematical equations, it is not observed to be determined by the players because the effects of their policies are influenced by the behaviour of the other companies which they do not control and cannot predict. Indeed it is not uncommon for one company, over a short period of play, to gain a strong impression that the effect of price on market share is the precise opposite of the actual effect.

This could occur for instance if the company concerned is lowering price at the same time as keeping marketing and research expenditure constant and if the other companies are keeping prices stable and increasing marketing and research expenditure. In certain circumstances this could cause the company lowering its price to lose some share of the market. This illustrates one feature of these models which is very valuable for training purposes. They force people to think of the combined effect of all the factors in the situation and not to concentrate on narrow aspects.

The time-lag effect in business decisions, which is a very important one, is allowed for by only allowing marginal changes in the decision choices for each team from period to period. This forces a long-range viewpoint on the team that wants to make any major changes in expenditure. The form used for this game, and the range of marginal choices at a given period, is shown in Figure 28.

With the McKinsey model, often called the Harvard game because it was first publicized in the *Harvard Business Review*, the sales effort is made, not by allocating a proportion of financial resources, as in the A.M.A. model, but by sending a number of salesmen to specified customers to effect a sale. The probability of achieving a sale is determined by advertising and by research expenditures. The chance element of the game is obtained by using random number tables to decide whether a sale is realized or not in a given circumstance and to determine whether the research effort expended has resulted in a product improvement.

The time-lag effect is introduced in a physical sense by causing time to elapse between the hiring of salesmen and their use in the field and between the scheduling of production and plant and their availability. This game requires the use of a game board for each team as shown in Figure 30.

The market potential at any time is determined in a similar fashion to that for the A.M.A. model, except that the potential is distributed

STATEMENT OF ASSETS
YEAR 1   QUARTER 4

	TOTAL $	NET CHANGE $
CASH	5,673,425	102,655
STOCK (55,030 Units at $4.437)	247,718	158,099
PLANT INVESTMENT (1,100,000 Units at $5.00)	5,500,000	110,000
TOTAL ASSETS	11,421,143	450,754

ANNUAL STATEMENTS
YEAR

	Company 1 $	Company 2 $	Company 3 $	Company 4 $	Company 5 $
	5,673,425	5,410,212	4,993,915	5,106,187	5,197,442
	247,718	397,960	385,143	489,683	498,503
	5,500,000	5,540,000	5,270,000	5,340,000	5,450,000
	11,421,143	11,243,172	10,649,058	10,935,870	11,145,945

INCOME STATEMENT

	$	$
SALES INCOME: 1,014,300 Units at	5.35	5,426,505
COST OF GOODS SOLD AND OPERATING EXPENSES:		
COST OF GOODS PRODUCED	4,658,650	
MARKETING AND R. & D.	135,000	
PLANT INVESTMENT	450,000	5,243,650
OTHER INCOME (Plant Disposal)		182,855
NET INCOME		182,855

MARKET INFORMATION

	Company 1	Company 2	Company 3	Company 4	Company 5
PRICE ($)	5.35	5.15	5.05	5.10	5.10
SHARE OF MARKET	20.70				
TOTAL MARKET (Units)	4,900,000				
POTENTIAL SALES (Units)					

OPERATING AND DECISION INFORMATION FOR NEXT PERIOD (YEAR 2; QUARTER 1)

UNIT COST OF PRODUCTION	($)	4.559	4.542	4.512	4.489	4.470	4.455	4.439	4.427	4.415
UNITS OF PRODUCTION		835,000	875,000	915,000	955,000	990,000	1,020,000	1,050,000	1,075,000	1,100,000
COST OF PRODUCTION	($)	3,806,765	3,974,250	4,128,480	4,286,995	4,425,300	4,544,100	4,660,950	4,750,025	4,856,500
MARKETING	($)	300,000	310,000	320,000	330,000	340,000	350,000	360,000		
R. & D.	($)	115,000	120,000	125,000	130,000	135,000	140,000	145,000		
ADDITIONAL PLANT INVESTMENT (Units)		14,000	16,000	18,000	20,000	22,000	24,000	26,000		
PRICE	($)	5.15	5.20	5.25	5.30	5.35	5.40	5.45	5.50	5.55
PLANT DISPOSAL (In Units)		Nil								

Fig. 28

89

3 _____ Company _____ Quarter _1_ _____ Year _4_

DISPOSITION OF CASH

		DEBIT		CREDIT	
		£			£
	Salaries (1,000)	9,000	Beginning Cash		43,750
	Hiring	5,000			
	Advertising (4)	6,000	A/R Collection		40,000
	R. & D.	10,000			
	Staff Work	5,000	A/R Factored		—
	Factoring	—			
	TOTAL EXPENSES	35,000	Loan		—
			TOTAL INCOME		83,750
	Plant Investment	—			
	Loan Repayment	—			
	Work in Process				
	(Sched. last qtr.)				
	Fixed Cost £6,000				
	Variable Cost (5) £15,000				
	Total £21,000	21,000	TOTAL OUTGO		56,000
	TOTAL OUTGO	56,000	ENDING CASH BALANCE		27,750

SALES VISITS indicate visit by ticks, so:

[✓]

[ ] 1
[ ] 2
[ ] 3
[ ] 4
[☒] 5
[ ] 6
[ ] 7
[ ] 8
[ ] 9
[ ] 10
[ ] 11
[ ] 12
[ ] 13
[ ] 14

PROFIT AND LOSS ACCOUNT

	Units	£	£
SALES	7		66,500
STOCK			
Opening	8	33,700	
Production (= WIP last qtr.)	5	21,000	

				13	34,700	
Total Stock						
Average Stock Cost	£4,200			7	29,400	29,400
Units Sold (at av. cost)				6	25,300	
Closing Inventory	.	.	.			37,100
GROSS PROFIT	.	.	.			35,000
TOTAL EXPENSES (see DEBITS)	.					
NET PROFIT	.	.	.			2,100

15	☐	
16	☐	
17	☒	
18	☐	
19	☐	
20	☒	
21	☑	1
22	☑	3
23	☑	3
24	☐	

TOTAL | 7 |

TOTAL ASSETS

Total Assets Last Quarter	.	£406,950
		£
Ending Cash Balance	.	27,750
Accounts Receivable	.	50,000
		10,000
	.	28,500
	.	66,500
Stock	Closing	25,300
	W.I.P.	21,000
Plant	.	180,000
TOTAL ASSETS	.	409,050
CHANGE IN TOTAL ASSETS	.	+2,100

PRICE AND SCHEDULING DECISIONS

Price	.	£9,500
Amount scheduled	.	4

SALESMEN'S RESIGNATIONS

No. of Salesmen in field	.	5
No. of Salesmen resigned	.	0

FIG. 29

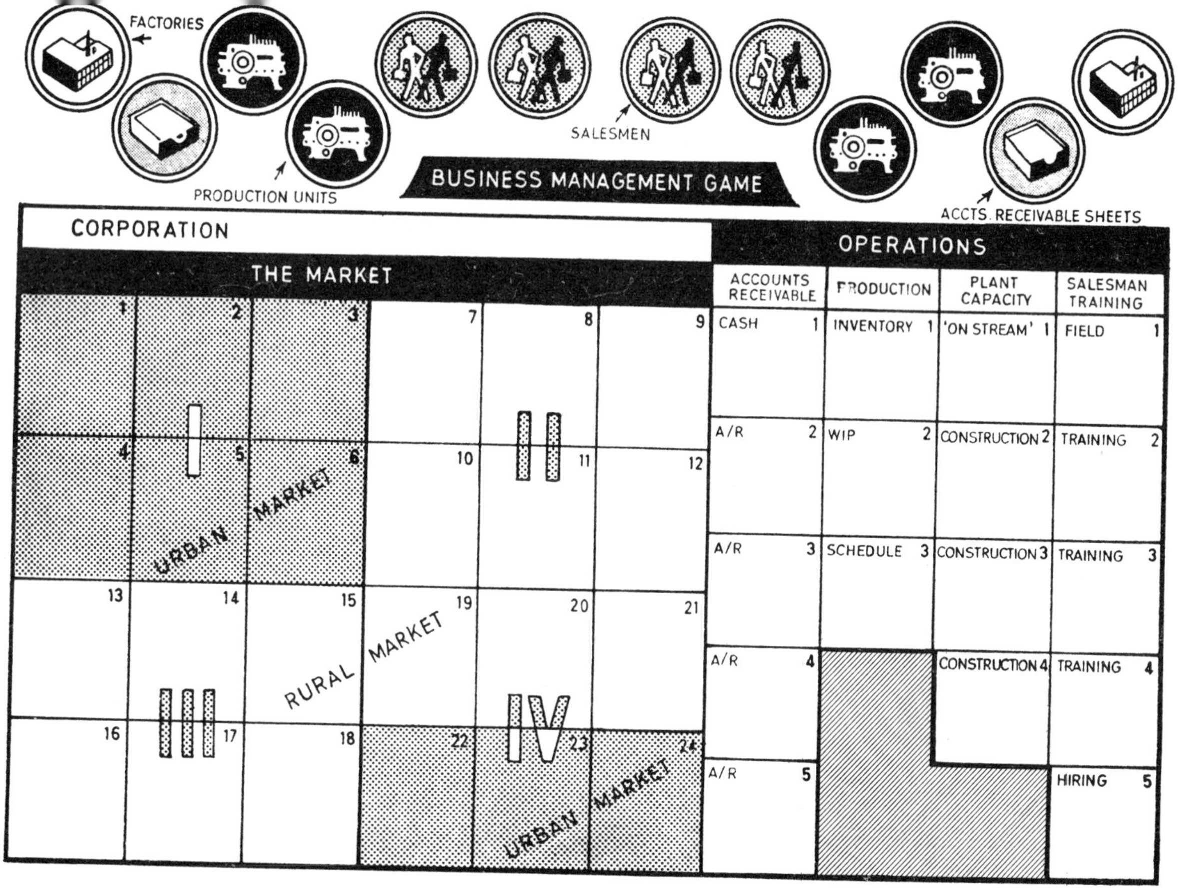
FACTORIES
PRODUCTION UNITS
SALESMEN
ACCTS. RECEIVABLE SHEETS
BUSINESS MANAGEMENT GAME
CORPORATION
THE MARKET
OPERATIONS
ACCOUNTS RECEIVABLE
PRODUCTION
PLANT CAPACITY
SALESMAN TRAINING
CASH 1
INVENTORY 1
'ON STREAM' 1
FIELD 1
A/R 2
WIP 2
CONSTRUCTION 2
TRAINING 2
A/R 3
SCHEDULE 3
CONSTRUCTION 3
TRAINING 3
A/R 4
CONSTRUCTION 4
TRAINING 4
A/R 5
HIRING 5
URBAN MARKET
RURAL MARKET
URBAN MARKET
I
II
III
IV
1
2
3
4
5
6
7
8
9
10
11
12
13
14
15
16
17
18
19
20
21
22
23
24

FIG. 30

among the available customers in a random fashion. The form used by the teams for recording the sales and financial results is shown in Figure 29.

Both models have advantages and disadvantages. The A.M.A. game has a smaller chance element than the Harvard game, but the computing of the results is more difficult. For rapid use of the A.M.A. model, say the simulation of six years in a day, an electronic computer is required. With the Harvard model six years can be played in a day by using desk calculators and experienced girl operators.

These models clearly will not simulate any particular company's situation as they are designed at present. To set up such a model is an exercise for the company concerned. What the games will do however is to provide valuable experience for training and selection purposes.

The first A.M.A. type game played in the Glacier Metal Co. produced some interesting results as shown graphically in Figure 31. As a result of inexperience the structure of the game was such that price had very little influence on market share or on total market. It was thus to the benefit of each team to raise prices as fast as possible within the limits laid down by the marginal constraints introduced for time-lag purposes.

Figure 31 shows how the prices of the five competing teams varied during the game. Each period represents one quarter of a year. Not until two 'years' elapsed did the teams learn that the market was insensitive to price and follow a wholehearted policy of increasing prices. Even then team 3, the team from the sales organization, raised its prices less rapidly than those of the other teams.

Appendix 2 shows the kind of document which must be given to each team to provide the necessary information for play and create the appropriate atmosphere. The game illustrated is played on the Harvard game board.

Playing these games between different sections of the same company provides valuable lessons as to the guiding philosophy behind each of these sections' policies. One finds, as above, that the sales organization team tends to keep prices low. A research organization team tends to experiment, perhaps not always wisely. A production control team tends to concentrate on inventory stability and overlook opportunities for increasing sales. With these narrow conceptions exposed in the genuinely competitive atmosphere of a business game each section of

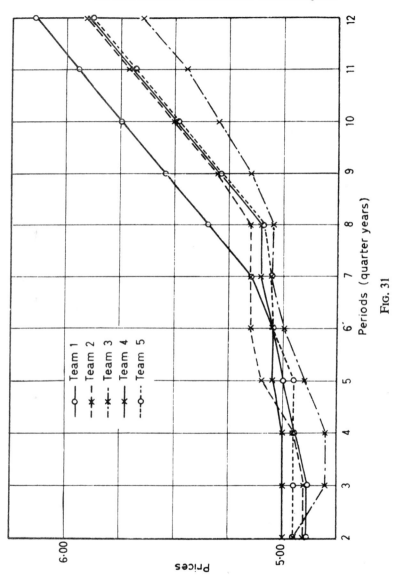

Fig. 31

Price behaviour in AMA game.

the company learns the necessity to take an overall view and appreciate more fully the need for sales forecasts in regulating production, the value of research in promoting sales, the necessity for reconciling apparently conflicting objectives and so on. As one work study manager said after finishing a game, 'I feel much more sympathy for my managing director now.'

These models can be used with great effect to test out O.R. policies and even to train O.R. workers! They have the virtue of organizational flexibility also in that intensive sessions of play can be carried out over one or two days of complete separation from normal duties or longer periods of play can be arranged without distraction from normal work, the players making their decisions in the time they would usually spend on crossword puzzles, and then sending the results to a central agency to be computed and returned for further decisions in due course.

At the Sixth Annual International Meeting of the American Institute of Management Science, held in Paris in September 1959, many examples of business games and the experience to be learned from them were described by both British and American authors.

Cybernetics

Most industrial operations need regulation and substantial strides have been made in recent years in understanding the nature of complex control systems. The approach has been to combine the mechanistic outlook of the electronic expert and servo-mechanism engineer with the organic knowledge of the biologist and neurologist into the new science of cybernetics.

This may be defined as the study of control systems in man and machine and the relation between them. In the words of Stafford Beer, 'Cybernetic systems are complex, interacting, probabilistic networks such as brains, markets, living organisms, industries, battles. Cyberneticians undertake the study of control in all these and many other contexts. How are such large systems organized? They seem to be cohesive, self regulating, and stable, yet adaptive to change and capable of learning from experience.'

From the work of cyberneticians two important control principles have emerged, one is that of error-actuated feedback, the other is homeostasis. The feedback principle can best be illustrated in one of its simplest forms, that of driving a car. The driver aims at a certain position on the road and checks after a few seconds if that position has been attained. If the difference between the desired position and the actual position is great enough an appropriate adjustment is made to the steering wheel, the new position is checked after a further few seconds and the cycle is repeated. The significance of this operation is that the error between the actual and required position is fed back to the driver and action is taken on the size of the error. This is what is meant by error actuated feedback.

The inexperienced driver, determined to permit himself the minimum amount of wander, will take corrective action on the smallest observed deviation and will make the amount of correction equal to the error. Thus the tyro's steering wheel is continually a-wobble and, as is well known, the result of his efforts is to wander about the road more than a skilled man.

The experienced driver knows, firstly, that certain errors in position are quite random and are accidental ones due to variations in road contour or other chance causes, and might well be self-corrected at the next bump. These deviations he ignores and thus steers a smoother course than the learner. Secondly, he knows that when a deviation is serious enough to take into account the correction he makes should be somewhat less than the error to avoid the risk of over-correction. He thus gradually restores the vehicle on to its original course. The dangers of making the feedback equal to the error are well illustrated in temperature controllers which exhibit the familiar phenomenon of 'hunting'.

Homeostasis is the property which all living organisms have of making use of error-actuated feedback to adjust their metabolism to changing environmental conditions, so that certain essential parameters remain constant. The blood temperature of a healthy reader of this book stays constant at 98·4° F. whether he be reading it in tropical humidity or sub-zero frost. A homeostatic mechanism is one which itself responds to the error actuated feedback instead of relying on an outside agent such as the car driver.

The principle is clearly an important one for industry. The environment of many industrial processes is continually changing. The raw materials vary, the process conditions change, the quality of the operating workers may deteriorate. If nothing else alters the plant itself is ageing and this can cause changes in the quality of the product. Few readers of this book will not have experienced the sudden appearance of new and complex problems on old-established processes. These are just symptoms of changes in the process which were not detected and rectified by subtle homeostatic procedures, but were allowed to accumulate until their presence could no longer be ignored.

The application of error actuated feedback and homeostasis to industrial operations is a difficult job. The manager of a process is not driving a car, able to see the road ahead, he is in the position a car driver would be in if he only had a glimpse of the road five miles back every few minutes or so. The analogy cannot be stretched too far obviously, but more O.R. will have to be carried out before these principles can be applied to the management function.

The approach is twofold. One way is to build the feedback and homeostasis into the organizational structure so that the appropriate observations are made and the corrections introduced by a human agency. The other is to design process machines which can do the job.

The first method offers more scope for advance on a short-term basis and one process known to me is operating on these principles. Observations are taken on a comprehensive scale and with sufficient frequency to enable any significant process changes to be detected. The limits within which the plant personnel can make changes themselves are clearly laid down but in such a way as not to inhibit development. When changes of a certain magnitude occur then outside technical help must be invoked. In this way adequate feedback at all levels of the process operation is ensured and the homeostatic experience of the plant operators with their knowledge of intimate detail and that of the technicians with their specialist training is utilized to the full. The use of cybernetic principles also helps in clarifying the organizational aspects of process control.

Other companies have also inaugurated cybernetic schemes based on organization structure. The best known one is that designed by Beer, and this too requires the collection and constant analysis of a large amount of information. Industry tends to fight shy of schemes which require a large amount of information because data collecting can be very expensive. It should be noted, however, as explained in the chapter on Information Theory, that the adequacy of a control system depends upon the amount of information contained in it. To confirm this, see how accurately you can drive a car by only looking at the road every two minutes. In many cases it may be more expensive *not* to have the information than to collect it.

The second method of advance, that of designing a machine, may overcome the problem of providing information and analysing it because this will very largely be done by the machine itself at little or no extra cost. The design and manufacture of such a machine will of course be a very comprehensive task, and one which is at present only being tackled specifically by one industrial group in this country, i.e. at the United Steel Co.

That such machines can exist has been demonstrated theoretically by Ashby, and a machine that exhibits a lot of the necessary properties is one now being produced by the Solartron Group for teaching Hollerith card punch operations. The machine sets the exercises for the pupil and adjusts itself to the pupil's characteristics in a cybernetic manner, concentrating on the learner's weaknesses or speeding up the exercises to the limits of the pupil's capacity.

That these machines will come there is no doubt. They will have many properties which are very desirable in control systems – continuous feedback, rapid response, an ability to recognize patterns better than do human beings, the capacity to explore numerous alternatives without exhaustion and so on. Before the machines are available, however, there is a lot that the O.R. worker can do in applying the same principles on an organizational basis so that industry can make much more effective use of the control information it has, and be encouraged to obtain further information where it is economically advantageous to do so.

One such cybernetic principle, which it is useful to expand on a little at this stage, is the 'Black Box' principle. In cybernetics a 'Black Box' is a system which is too complex to be understood fully in the existing state of knowledge. Most companies are 'Black Boxes'. The economic system of this country certainly is. To attempt to understand the nature of the interrelations inside a 'Black Box' in order to inaugurate the necessary feedback controls can be a fruitless and unrewarding task, and one in fact that had better be left unattempted, because if the system is complex enough the control may be achieved in a far simpler way.

The 'Black Box' principle in cybernetics states that the behaviour of the complex system is discovered merely by studying the relationship between the input and the output and not by considering what happens inside the 'Black Box.' By studying the relationship between input and output one can often learn what changes are needed to the input to achieve a given change in output, and thus learn all that is needed to control the system.

As an example of this principle applied in a very simple manner a production controller was once worried about how to schedule a tool room. The nature of the work in the tool room seemed to vary considerably in size, complexity, in time taken for machining and so on. To apply conventional production control methods would have necessitated the employment of about three or four clerks to record all the necessary information inside the 'Black Box'.

The production controller noticed, however, that when the tool room was fully occupied it produced about forty jobs per week. This number varied somewhat of course, but the average stayed fairly constant at forty. Thus he argued that an input of forty jobs per week should keep the tool room fully occupied and ensure an output of forty jobs per week. He could also schedule the plant developments which were waiting for the tool room to complete its work on the basis of a tool room output of forty jobs per week. This simple rule proved very effective and is an illustration of how the 'Black Box' principle in cybernetics can be used to control situations which if gone into deeply may seem very complex.

A further example of the 'Black Box' principle is the treatment of mental patients. The human brain is certainly a 'Black Box', and while a great deal of neurological research is going on to understand the mechanism of the brain, progress in treatment is also being made by observing patients' responses to stimuli.

Information theory

This is akin to cybernetics and will have but brief mention in this book, because its industrial applications are as yet few. It is worth mentioning, however, because modern industry depends for its operation upon the efficiency of its internal and external communication systems. The middle manager in particular spends most of his time in communication (see Burns) and surprisingly little, perhaps too little, time in thinking and planning. It is thus most important for industry to understand the properties of its communication systems, for without this understanding they will be used inefficiently.

How often, for example, when some grave mistake has been made in a firm, sufficiently serious to warrant a post-mortem, has it been found to be due, not to gross inefficiency on the part of any individual but to a failure in the communication system?

The properties of communication systems have been studied very fully by telephone engineers and the first formal publication of results was by Shannon. He originally used the title 'Communication Theory', but because the notion of a quantitative measure of information was central to his theme the name 'Information Theory' has come into use.

Shannon's results were as follows:

1. Information cannot be transmitted at any arbitrarily great rate over a given communication system. It is possible, given all the necessary properties of a communication system, to calculate the maximum rate at which information can be transmitted.

2. Communications made in a system are not entirely independent of one another and do not occur with a completely random distribution. In English speech for instance the letter *e* occurs with much more frequency than the letter *k* and we can often complete an unfinished word or sentence with a high degree of exactitude. This property that some information is expected with a greater frequency than other information can be used in the design of a system.

3. There is always random interference, i.e. noise, in any communication system. This occurs in telephone speech of course and even with written messages there is a finite probability of them going astray.

The results of Shannon can be expressed mathematically and used for the design of telephone circuits. At present they cannot readily be used for the design and improvement of business communication systems, but the time will probably come when they can be.

Even the general principles can be useful to managers, however. They must not expect information to be transmitted through their organization at great speed without errors occurring. This is a warning against the panic actions which are frequent in some organizations and often disastrous. Conversely, if a manager wishes to ensure that information is transmitted error free, then he must give plenty of time for its transmission.

For a message to be really clear and free from ambiguity it must contain a lot of apparently unnecessary and redundant information. This is because not all the information can be absorbed and thus it is

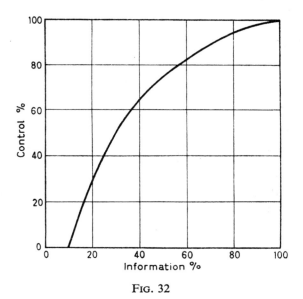

FIG. 32

Relationship between control and information.

necessary to put in surplus information. Not for nothing did the negro preacher say, 'I tells 'em what I'm going to tell 'em; I tell 'em; then I tells 'em what I've told 'em.'

Finally the manager must expect that information will be lost from his organization and will need to be replaced. This is well known to every librarian's filing clerk. It may seem to be due to inefficiency and mistakes, but it is an inevitable phenomenon of every information system and should be recognized as such.

There is a relationship between information theory and cybernetics. The degree of control of a system is proportional to the logarithm of the information in this system. This relationship is shown in Figure 32, and it serves to emphasize what was said in the section on cybernetics that no system can be adequately controlled without sufficient information. At present we do not know how much information is necessary to ensure an adequate degree of control, but with development of information theory our knowledge of control may improve. For further reading the books of Cherry should be consulted.

Network analysis

One of the consequences of the realization that information is essential for control purposes, and that the greater the information the better the control, has been the development of network analysis for planning and scheduling. The use of this technique has expanded greatly in the last few years and it is now one of the most powerful means of controlling complex scheduling operations such as the building of a new factory, the maintenance programme of complex plant and the marketing of new products.

The scheduling problems appropriate for network analysis are different from those considered earlier on pages 27 and 69. In these earlier pages the optimum use of available resources for scheduling continuous and largely repetitive operations was considered. In network analysis the deployment of available resources for the completion of a non-repetitive task within the minimum time or for the minimum cost is studied. As the use and experience of network analysis grows, and the scope of linear programming widens, the distinction between these two types of scheduling becomes blurred, but at present they are still fairly clear cut.

A simple illustration of the purpose of network analysis can be given in the following way. Every morning, say, you toast three pieces of toast in a toaster which will take two pieces of bread at a time. (Although, you may argue, this is a repetitive task it is not a continuously repetitive one in the assembly line sense and hence it is appropriate for consideration by network analysis and not linear programming.) The schedule for the operation may be as follows:

	Seconds
Toast one side of pieces A and B	30
Toast other side of pieces A and B	30
Toast one side of piece C	30
Toast other side of piece C	30
Total time	120

The whole schedule could be shortened, however, if, as shown in a famous wartime advertisement for fuel saving, the toasting sequence were as follows:

	Seconds
Toast one side of pieces A and B	30
Toast one side of C and other side of A	30
Toast other side of B and C	30
Total time	90

Although this is a very trivial example of how time can be saved by optimizing the logical sequence of events, many similar opportunities occur in large-scale development and maintenance programmes and can be overlooked but for the rigorous discipline imposed by network analysis.

A slightly more complex example, involving multi-activity analysis, could follow the toasting sequence when you get out your car and drive to work.

The schedule for the operation may be:

	Seconds
Walk to garage doors	10
Open garage door	5
Walk to car	5
Enter and start car	10
Drive car out of garage	5
Walk back to garage	5
Shut garage doors	5
Walk back to car and drive off	10
Total time	55

Now if you were desperately short of time you would ask your wife to open the garage doors and the schedule would then be:

Your Wife	*Seconds*	*You*	*Seconds*
Walk to garage doors	10	Walk to car by back	
Open garage doors	5	door of garage	10
Wait	5	Enter and start car	5
		Drive car out of garage	5

The total time you have spent is reduced to 20 seconds and hence there is a saving to you of 35 seconds. If your wife were to close the garage doors and join you in the car only a further 15 seconds would be taken, still leaving a saving of 20 seconds. The total time spent by you *and* your wife in the whole operation is still only 55 seconds and thus has, in total, been no more costly in time despite the overall saving of 20 seconds. It is this kind of planning, together with that shown in the first example, which, on a vastly larger scale, is reported to have cut the completion time of the Polaris missile system from 7 to 5 years and reduced unproductive time on maintenance shut downs in chemical works.

How is it done? It is not possible within the scope of a few hundred words to give a very adequate answer. This has been done most ably in a recent textbook by Battersby. A further example will be given, however, to demonstrate some of the main principles.

Suppose you are having your house painted (again, you will see, a recurring but not continuously repetitive task), the schedule may be similar to the following:

		Days
A	Clean gutters	1
B	Paint inside gutters	1
C	Paint outside gutters	$1\frac{1}{2}$
D	Wash paint first floor	$\frac{1}{2}$
E	Burn off where necessary	$\frac{1}{2}$
F	Sandpaper surface	$\frac{1}{2}$
G	Final wash	$\frac{1}{2}$
H	Priming coat of paint	1
I	Undercoat	2

J	Top coat of paint	2
K	Wash paint ground floor	$\frac{1}{2}$
L	Burn off where necessary	$\frac{1}{2}$
M	Sandpaper surface	$\frac{1}{2}$
N	Final wash	$\frac{1}{2}$
O	Priming coat of paint	1
P	Undercoat	2
Q	Top coat of paint	2
	Total	$17\frac{1}{2}$

This schedule assumes that only one man is engaged on the job. You may decide to save money and shorten the total time by doing all the preparation yourself and only employ a skilled man for the actual painting. You may even try a little classical scheduling by making up the Gantt chart shown in Figure 33 below.

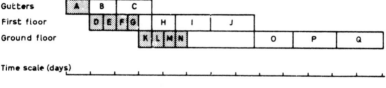

FIG. 33

This type of chart shows how the total time can be reduced to $13\frac{1}{2}$ days, $12\frac{1}{2}$ days of which needs the employment of full-time painter, the shaded sections, representing preparation work, being done by yourself.

The weakness of the traditional type of Gantt chart is that, except in simple cases, such as shown above, it is not easy to establish the interconnection of events – such as that painting cannot start until preparation is finished – nor is it easy to see which is the critical path of the scheduling operation. The critical path is the one to which attention must be paid if there is to be any shortening of the total schedule.

In network analysis the interconnection of events is shown by arrows and the critical path is readily discernible. In network notation the house painting schedule would appear as shown in

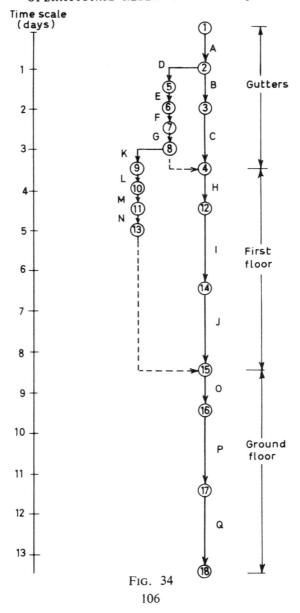

FIG. 34

Figure 34. This chart shows two things more clearly than the Gantt chart. It shows that the preparation jobs D, E, F, G and K, L, M, N must be completed before the priming paint tasks H and O can be started and that there is, in fact, slack time available in the preparation jobs, shown by the dotted lines. It also shows that the critical path through the network, i.e. that in which there is no slack time, is 1 – 2 – 3 – 4 – 12 – 14 – 15 – 16 – 17 – 18.

Figure 34 clearly demonstrates therefore that there is no point initially in taking steps to shorten the preparation time because there is slack time available already. If it is required to shorten the completion time then additional skilled painting labour must be provided. It is clear also from the diagram that there is little purpose in employing extra painting skill earlier than point 13 unless both painters can be working on the same floor at the same time, or unless the preparation time can be considerably shortened. If both painters can be working on the same floor at the same time then an additional painter can be usefully employed from point 8.

Suppose point 13 is the earliest at which a second painter can be introduced, then he will complete tasks O, P and Q 5 days after point 13 and thus the total time will be shortened to 10 days. If he is able to start at point 8 then the total time will be shortened to $8\frac{1}{4}$ days. If additional preparation help is provided then the total time can be shortened to $6\frac{3}{4}$ days.

If time is all-important and cost no consideration, within the limitations imposed by, say, the physical impossibility of having more than two painters and two preparers working on the house, then the schedule would be reduced to $6\frac{3}{4}$ days and the network diagram would look like Figure 35. The numbers at the side of each arrow indicate the number of men working simultaneously. There is now no critical path because there is now slack time and hence, with the resources available, $6\frac{1}{4}$ days is the shortest possible time. It is, it will be noted, just half the original time.

It may not, however, be an economical solution. If both painters are kept on the same floor throughout, instead of being split at point 13, then the total time taken is still $6\frac{3}{4}$ days but only one man is needed for preparation from point 8 onwards. The reader can construct the appropriate network and verify this. If the house-

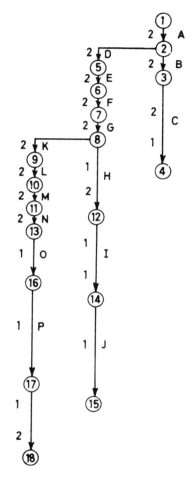

FIG. 35

owner is prepared to do preparation work himself, without charge, then clearly it is better for him to employ an extra man for preparation for only a short time.

It is interesting to compare the costs of the various schedules. If x is the cost per day of a man for preparation and $2x$ the cost per day of a painter, then it can be shown that the schedules in Figures 34 and 35 each cost $30x$ but that the schedule taking 10 days costs $33x$. Hence cost as well as time considerations can assist in choosing between feasible schedules. A very simple illustration of this is given in Battersby's book and also in an article by him in *The Accountant*, August 18th, 1962.

Network analysis is known by many names and initials, P. E. R. T. (Programme Evaluation and Review Technique); P.E.R.T./COST; C.P.M. (Critical Path Method); P. E. P. (Programme Evaluation Procedure); L.E.S.S. (Least Cost Estimating and Scheduling); S.C.A.N.S. (Scheduling and Control by Automated Network Systems), and numerous others. The principles of all these are very similar however. Very large networks are now being analysed. That for part of Polaris, with the critical path marked as a dark line, is shown in Figure 36. Uncertainty in estimated times has now been

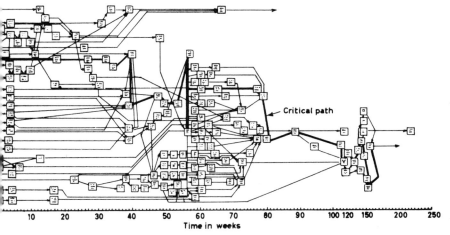

Critical path

Time in weeks

Reproduced from *Operations Research in Research and Development*, Wiley 1963, by courtesy
[of the editor, B. V. Dean

FIG. 36

allowed for by the use of statistical method, and computer programmes are available for calculating critical paths under numerous
circumstances. The technique has very wide scope and it is to be
hoped that many enterprises concerned with construction and
development work will adopt it. Its use is being extended into the
planning of research programmes involving uncertainty of outcome
of decisions (see Brown).

Evolutionary operation

This is not really a technique of O.R., it belongs to Industrial Statistics,
but its concept has so much in common with those of O.R. and it is a
technique of such value to the industrial manager to whom this book
is addressed that there is ample justification for discussing it here.

The idea is due to Box and his colleagues, and his published work
should be consulted by those who wish to apply the technique.
Basically, the suggestion of Box was that industrial processes should
not solely yield products, they should also provide information. How
important this information is has been stressed in the sections on

Cybernetics and Information Theory. The more information that a process can be made to yield the greater the degree of control.

The information is produced by evolutionary operation in the following manner. Instead of keeping rigidly to one method of operating the process, the operating conditions are allowed to vary sufficiently far from the usual ones to enable the consequences of the departure to be assessed and yet not sufficiently far for those consequences to be harmful.

As an illustration, consider a chemical process in which the temperature of reaction, the pressure and the concentration of a given reactant are important factors. They are usually controlled, let us say, at 250° C., 50 p.s.i. and 42 gm/litre respectively. These have been considered the optimum levels of these factors, possibly as a result of laboratory or pilot plant experiments. It would not do any harm, however, if the temperature varied from 240–260° C., the pressure from 45–55 p.s.i. and the concentration from 40–44 gm./litre.

Therefore, instead of operating the process continually at 250° C., 50 p.s.i. and 42 gm./litre, it can be operated safely, but perhaps with some sacrifice of efficiency, at each of the following conditions in turn.

Temperature (°C.)	Pressure (p.s.i.)	Concentration (gm./litre)
240	45	40
260	45	40
240	55	40
260	55	40
240	45	44
260	45	44
240	55	44
260	55	44

together with the normal operating conditions of 250° C., 50 p.s.i. and 42 g. gm./litre.

The difference in results, be it output, or quality, or cost between each of the above alternative processes, and the usual one may be small, indeed to make it practicable for the process manager to operate these alternatives without running risks, they may have to be small and in one single trial of each of them the difference may be too small to be considered worth while or may not even be detected in view of the usual random variations of process results. However, if the above cycle of treatments is repeated many times, then by reason of their repetition, any real differences will become detectable and significant in the statistical sense. Thus if one of the alternatives is a better way of operating the process than the standard one, a change can be made to this alternative and a further series of experiments around this new standard carried out.

This is illustrated diagrammatically below. Only two dimensions

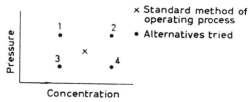

FIG. 37

are used for the illustration although in practice, by means of sophisticated statistical techniques, many factors can be varied simultaneously.

Suppose alternative 2 is eventually found to be the best one. This then becomes the new standard and a further series of alternatives tried as shown below.

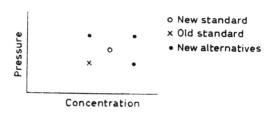

FIG. 38

Note that the old standard is included in the new trial, to check that it is not, after all, the best way of operating the process.

By means of these repeated trials, varying the process factors by small amounts around the standard conditions, and then choosing the optimum to form a new standard around which further controlled variation can be made, the process conditions will gradually evolve in the direction of the final optimum.

The process can thus be made to yield information about itself during relatively normal operations.

The costs of making these changes can be assessed and weighed against the advantages in the manner described by Box, but there is little doubt that the technique of evolutionary operation is not only an advantageous method of running a process but almost a necessary one. A process does not remain static, and the conventional kind of process engineering which attempts to lay down a rigid, once for all, standard of process operation is condemning the process to death.

Processes are evolving willy-nilly, and the way to keep in touch with the evolution is to operate the process in an evolutionary manner. At present such evolutionary operation must be arranged through a human agency. In future years it may be organized by cybernetic machinery.

Other Operational Research techniques

This book has so far dealt with twelve operational research techniques and their particular application in certain cases. These techniques do not of course represent the limit of an O.R. team's capabilities, nor are they the sum total of existing O.R. techniques. Other methods which could have been mentioned are – search theory, symbolic logic, Boolean algebra, and dynamic programming. Some techniques applied in O.R. are borrowed from other disciplines – actuarial theory and value theory for example. There are others being developed continually. Some are applicable in but a few rare cases. Others acquire the powerful sweep of queueing theory or simulation.

The point to make, however, is that O.R. is not just a collection of techniques, it is, as discussed earlier, an attitude of mind. The attitude of mind of the experimentalist who wishes to find logical causal relationships, albeit statistical ones, in the object of his study and then to use the results of his observations to gain greater control of the environment. Operational research is the scientific study of systems in business, just as natural science is the study of systems in nature. Business men will have to learn that they cannot gain increased control over their environment unless they carry out such study and do experiments. Mankind did not gain such control over Nature as he possesses without experiments. Operational Research methods, by constructing models and studying their behaviour, minimize the risks involved in such experimentation.

Many of the problems which harass industrial managers because they cut across the work of several specialities can be tackled by an O.R. group, especially if it includes, albeit temporarily, members of each speciality. The O.R. team acts as the catalyst which ensures that the work has a continuity which would be difficult to achieve otherwise in view of the other commitments of the managerial personnel involved.

An important aspect to emphasize once more in O.R. work is that although it often cuts across the work of several departments it is in no way set above these departments. It does not exist to judge but to discover. The decisions arising from O.R. investigations must always be made by the managers requesting the investigations. O.R. enhances management, it does not usurp it.

Very often the problems which arise in a manager's department could be tackled by the manager himself if he had more time and several of my investigations have closely followed the lines laid down by the requesting manager, because these were the best ones to follow. The presence of a team of people with an intimate knowledge of the company's operations, with a scientific outlook and with a training in the kind of analytical techniques described in this book can be a very valuable adjunct to the company.

REFERENCES

MATHEMATICAL STATISTICS

Two good readable introductions to statistical method are:
MORONEY, M. J. *Facts from Figures.* Penguin Books (1951)
REICHMANN, W. J. *Use and Abuse of Statistics.* Methuen (1962)
A more comprehensive book is:
DAVIES, O. L. (Ed.). *Statistical Methods in Research and Production,* 2nd ed. Oliver and Boyd (1949)

LINEAR PROGRAMMING

DOIG, A. *The Paper Trim Problem.* M.A. Thesis, Melbourne, Australia

MUIR, A. *The Application of Linear Programming to the Design of Animal Feeding Stuffs*. Business Computer Symposium, London (December 1958)

GARVIN, W. W., CRANDALL, J. B. J. and SHELLMAN, R. A. 'Applications of Linear Programming in the Oil Industry,' *Management Science* (July 1957)

CAPLIN, D. A. 'The Use of Digital Computers in Manning Plant Operations', *Trans. Inst. Chem. Eng.*, Vol. 36, p. 311 (1958)

DEAM, R. 'The Use of Linear Programming in Oil Refinery Operations,' *Process Control and Automation* (February 1959)

MORTON, G. and KAY, E. *Metalworking Production*, Vol. 99 (Dec. 23, 1955)

KAY, E. and DUCKWORTH, E. 'Linear Programming in Practice', *Applied Statistics*, Vol. 6, p. 26 (1957)

WYATT, J. K. 'Two Years of Linear Programming', *Operational Research Quarterly* Vol. 9, No. 2 (1958)

GOULD, S. 'A Method of Dealing with Certain Non-Linear Allocation Problems using the Transportation Technique', *Operational Research Quarterly* Vol. 10, No. 2 (1959)

BATTERSBY, A. 'Piping and Plant Design – Can Linear Programming Help?', *Manufacturing Chemist* (September 1958)

The standard works on the most common computational procedures for linear programming problems are:
CHARNES A., COOPER, W. W. and HENDERSON, A. *An Introduction to Linear Programming*. Chapman and Hall (1953)

GASS, S. I. *Linear Programming*. McGraw-Hill (1958)

A useful introductory book is:
VAJDA, S. *An Introduction to Linear Programming and the Theory of Games*. Methuen (1960)

QUEUEING THEORY

ROBINSON, F. D. and DUCKWORTH, W. E. 'An Application of Queueing Theory to the Speed of Estimating', *First International Conference on Operational Research*. English Universities Press (1957)

DOIG, A. 'A Bibliography on the Theory of Queues', *Biometrika*, Vol. 44, p. 490 (December 1957)

MORSE, P. M. *Queues, Inventories and Maintenance*. Wiley (1958)

SIMULATION

WYATT, J. K. 'Prediction by Computer', *Data Processing*, Vol. 1, No. 3 (1959)

HARLING, J. 'Simulation Techniques in Operations Research – A Review', *Operations Research*, Vol. 6, No. 3 (1958)

A general programme for industrial simulation has been prepared by the Operational Research Department of the United Steel Co.

A comprehensive review of simulation is *Simulation, Managements Laboratory* published by Simulation Associates, P.O. Box 36, Groton, Connecticut.

STOCK AND PRODUCTION CONTROL MODELS

HOLT, C. C., MODIGLIANI, F. and SIMON, H. A. 'A Linear Decision Rule for Production and Employment Scheduling'. O.N.R. *Research Memorandum*, No. 30 (May 1955), D.S.I.R. P.B. 125029; also *Management Science* (October 1955)

BATTERSBY, A. 'Production Control by Electronic Computer', *Chemistry & Industry*, 1958, p. 1488

BATTERSBY, A. *A Guide to Stock Control*. BIM/Pitman (1962)

BURBIDGE, J. L. 'A New Approach to Production Control', *The Institution of Production Engineers Journal* (May 1958)

JOHNSON, S. M. 'Optimal Two and Three-Stage Production Scheduling', *Naval Research Logistics Quarterly (U.S.A.)*, Vol. 1, No. 1

FORRESTER, J. W. 'Industrial Dynamics', *Harvard Business Review* (July–August 1958)

COLLCUTT, R. H., BANBURY, J., MASSEY, R. G. and WARD, R. A. 'A Method of Fixing Desirable Stock Levels and of Stock Control', *Operational Research Quarterly*, Vol. 10, No. 2 (June 1959)

SALVESON, M. E. 'A Problem in Optimal Machine Loading', *Management Science* (April 1956)

MORAN, P. A. P. *Theory of Storage*. Methuen (1960)

MAGEE, J. F. *Production Planning and Inventory Control*. McGraw Hill

BROWN, W. B. and JAQUES, E. *Product Analysis Pricing*. Heinemann (1964)

DECISION THEORY

MILLS, E. S. 'The Theory of Inventory Decisions', *Econometrika*, Vol. 25, No. 2, p. 222 (April 1957)

GOOD, I. J. 'Rational Decisions', *J. R. Stat. Soc. B.* Vol. 14, p. 115 (1952)

Two interesting books are:

THRALL, R. M., COOMBS, C. H. and DAVIS, R. L. *Decision Processes.* Chapman and Hall (1954)

DAVIDSON, D. and SUPPES, P. *Decision Making, An Experimental Approach.* Stanford University Press, California (1957)

GAME THEORY

WILLIAMS, J. D. *The Compleat Strategyst.* McGraw Hill (1957)

OPERATIONAL GAMING

The A.M.A. game is described in *Operations Research* (August 1957) and the Harvard game in the *Harvard Business Review* (March–April 1958).

A recent book on the subject is:

GREENE, J. R. and SISSON, R. L. *Dynamic Management Decision Games.* Wiley (1959).

CYBERNETICS

GUILBAUD, G. T. *What is Cybernetics.* Heinemann (1959)

BEER, STAFFORD. *Cybernetics in Management.* English Universities Press (1959)

ASHBY, ROSS. *Introduction to Cybernetics.* Chapman and Hall (1957)

INFORMATION THEORY

BURNS, T. 'Management in Action', *Operational Research Quarterly*, Vol. 8, No. 2 (1957)

CHERRY, C. (Ed.) *Information Theory.* 2nd London Conference

CHERRY, C. *On Human Communication.* Chapman and Hall (1957)

BROWN, R. L. B.C.U.R.A. Gazette No. 52 (1965)

NETWORK ANALYSIS

BATTERSBY, A. *Network Analysis for Planning and Scheduling.* Macmillan (1964)

A useful book giving further information is:

DEAN, BURTON V. (Ed.) *Operations Research in Research and Development.* Wiley (1963)

116

EVOLUTIONARY OPERATION

BOX, G. E. P. 'Evolutionary Operation: A Method for Increasing Industrial Productivity', *Applied Statistics* (June 1957)

GENERAL

A complete bibliography of some 3000 papers on O.R. is:

'A comprehensive bibliography on Operations Research', *Publications in Operations Research*, No. 4. Chapman and Hall (1958)

Another bibliography which has been prepared is:

BATCHELOR, J. H. *Operations Research, An Annotated Bibliography.* St. Louis University Press (1959)

Quarterly international abstracts in O.R. are now being edited by J. H. Batchelor and can be obtained from the Operational Research Society, 64 Cannon Street, London E.C.4

Two books which contain examples of several O.R. techniques are:

BOWMAN, E. H. and FETTER, R. B. *Analyses of Industrial Operations.* Irwin, Illinois, U.S.A. (1959)

HOULDEN, B. T. *Some Techniques of Operational Research.* English Universities Press (1961)

PART III: THE ORGANIZATION OF OPERATIONAL RESEARCH

Because foresight is required the leader always has to be doing two apparently incompatible things. He has to encourage his administrators to promote order, to maintain established routines. At the same time he has to protect from their wrath the inventors, the crazy people to whom order is anathema and an established routine a challenge to change it, because it is from this lunatic fringe that he is most likely to derive something original.
. . . This conflict is one of the great paradoxes . . . The business that cannot resolve it will either go bankrupt tomorrow because it is too disorganized to get out the goods, or in five years' time because it is still trying to sell the same goods.

L. F. URWICK: *Leadership in the Twentieth Century*

Where Operational Research fits in

The proper siting of an O.R. Department in an industrial organization is a problem that itself deserves to be tackled by O.R. methods and this has been done. The correct location of any function in an organization is a difficult job unless the relationship between that function and other required functions has been clearly thought out. Twelve years of research has been carried out in the Glacier Metal Co., first by the Tavistock Institute of Human Relations, then by Dr Elliott Jaques. The work has been described by Wilfred Brown. I am indebted to these sources for the following ideas.

The work of a company consists essentially of three operations, Development, Production and Sales. Without any one of these it will cease to exist. Any one of these operational tasks requires three phases for its accomplishment, i.e. personnel, techniques and programmes. These are the three essential phases of work. No task can

118

be achieved without involving a person (automatic machines not excepted, since they are evolved by people), a technique, and a programme.

In a company with a clear-cut organizational structure the operating commands of Development, Production and Sales will be clearly differentiated and so will the staff functions of Personnel, Techniques and Programming. Operational Research in general has to do with the programming function in industry and all the methods described in this book will be found to apply to the programming problem; which is the balancing of the capacity of a company in terms of production plant, financial resources, development function and sales effort, with the demands made on it by customers, so as to produce the optimum result for the shareholders and employees. This is the system with which O.R. is concerned in optimizing.

Linear programming is not used for selecting personnel or for developing manufacturing techniques. It is used for optimizing the use of capacity. Queueing theory is not used for training people or for gaining metallurgical know-how, it is used for balancing demand and capacity. The actions people take in business games are not those concerned in the personnel or technical fields, they are the actions of a programmer.

Thus is O.R. concerned with programming, and the O.R. team should be responsible to the man in charge of the programming function. In a small firm he may be the managing director. So be it. In a small firm the O.R. team should probably be directly responsible to him because the managing director may be the only man who can see the system he is in charge of in sufficient outline for the value of O.R. to be appreciated.

In a company of more than, say, 1,000 employees, however, the managing director is likely to have delegated the programming function and the best place for the O.R. team is therefore one step removed from him. The difficulty is that in many cases it is not clear to whom this function has been delegated.

The first task of O.R. in such a firm might well be to have the programming function clarified so that one person can be made responsible for it and to whose group the O.R. team can clearly be attached. In other situations it may be attached to the person with the greatest degree of programming responsibility. In a single factory he may be the production controller. In a company he may be one of the directors or a general manager, or even the chief accountant. In any event the O.R. team will function most effectively if it is responsible to someone with authority to implement schemes which improve the efficiency of the programming function.

Some O.R. teams in industry are attached to research departments or other sections such as central administration, and are there to provide a service to those who wish it. This might sound very nice and genteel, and it does great credit to the personal relationships within any such organization that the O.R. team placed in this situation does a good job and gets many ideas accepted and into operation. But it says nothing for the managing director of such an organization that he allows such a practice to go on. He should not allow the efficiency of his organization in such a major field as programming to depend upon the good personal relationships of his staff.

He should clarify his organization, delegate one man for the programming task and see that the O.R. team is responsible to him. In the absence of such clarification O.R. work is unlikely to be fully effective and will depend for such success as it achieves on the expenditure of a lot of effort on personal persuasion.

How to start up Operational Research

The beginning of O.R. in an organization is a somewhat delicate task. The one thing to avoid is ballyhoo. Operational Research does not work miracles and to herald the arrival of an O.R. man or department as if it was the management panacea to end all management panaceas is to condemn it to impotence for some considerable time.

Operational Research depends for its success on the people who have to work the schemes having confidence that they will work. This applies notwithstanding the above remarks on personal relationships, because if no one else need be considered the programmer has to be, and he is usually a shrewd, able and experienced man.

It is a well-known fact of course that people in industry are happier and more efficient working schemes that they believe in than if they go sullenly following the dictates of higher authority.

It is thus best to commence O.R. on minor problems, say the production scheduling of a single product, the purchasing of a particular type of stores, a congestion situation in a small unit and so on. If possible the initial tasks should be those with a high probability of success using known O.R. techniques, so that confidence can be gained in the use of these techniques and in the people using them. Big jobs need a lot of data collection and interviews with many senior executives. These are difficult to conduct effectively without experienced staff who are accepted as such.

Herrmann and Magee have adequately defined the type of problem on which it is suitable to begin O.R. In their words:

"(1) There should be an opportunity for decision between alternative course of action.

"(2) There should be a real possibility for quantitative study and measurement. Thus, a preliminary study to provide bases for predicting the acceptance of fabric styles had to be quickly dropped in one case because of the inability to construct within a reasonable period an adequate quantitative description of the complexities of fabric, style, pattern and colour.

"(3) It should be possible to collect data. In one case, analysis of accounts receivable for the previous two years yielded the key to a knotty marketing problem. But, in another case, a study of maintenance problems was found to be uneconomical because of the lack of available records showing maintenance and breakdown histories on equipment.

"(4) It should be possible to evaluate results readily. In other words, the problem should not be so large that it is indefinite; there should be some specific aspect which lends itself to solution. Neither the analyst nor the most enthusiastic executive can expect O.R. activities to be supported on the basis of faith alone.

"The final choice is best made in co-operation with the research team. Executives have found it useful to map out the general area in advance; the research group can then comment on those aspects which are most amenable to study, to clear formulation of the problem, and to likelihood of progress with reasonable effort. On this basis a specific problem can be selected which meets the requirements both of the executive (for importance and use) and of the research group (for suitability of existing data for quantitative study).

"Much frustration and dissatisfaction can be avoided when the research team and the executives keep in mind each other's needs.

The research team must formulate a sufficiently understandable statement of the problem and method of attack to provide the executives with confidence in giving support. The executives, in turn, must recognize that in research advance specifications for a detailed programme including scope and goals are frequently difficult and usually meaningless; they must provide the group with access to the necessary data and people; and they must maintain contact with the work, guiding and redirecting it along the lines of greatest value as it develops."

Once O.R. has proved itself on simple tasks wider and wider problems can be tackled until O.R. is being fruitfully employed on programming problems affecting the whole of the company's operations.

This need not necessarily apply of course where an outside consultant is being employed to carry out an O.R. investigation. The size of job to be tackled by him must clearly depend upon the employer's assessment of his capabilities and a knowledge of the kind of job he has done for other firms.

How to find and train the staff

Good O.R. people are scarce and command appropriate salaries. In 1967 a manager of an O.R. department with from four to thirty people in it could expect a salary ranging from £3,500–£6,000 p.a. ($25,000–$50,000 in the U.S.A.). An O.R. investigator aged from 25 to 35 could expect a salary from £1,500–£3,000 p.a. ($10,000–$20,000 in the U.S.A.).

One way of starting up an O.R. Department is to attract an experienced O.R. investigator who wishes to start up on his own and let him build up the department within the company as the need for it is demonstrated.

Another way is to call in an outside firm of consultants to tackle particular jobs and to train either the employing company's existing staff or specially selected staff in O.R. techniques.

Yet a third way is to find a member of your staff who is interested in O.R. and seems capable of being good at it and send him away to be trained at one of the recognized courses listed by Kendal. A later list is now available from the Operational Research Society. On his return he may possibly be supported in his first few tasks by an outside consulting organization.

All these ways have been proved successful in different circumstances. The choice is clearly that of the individual firm.

REFERENCES

BROWN, W. B. D. *Exploration in Management.* Heinemann (1960)

HERRMANN, C. F. and MAGEE, J. F. 'Operations Research for Management', *Harvard Business Review*, p. 100 (July–August 1953)

KENDAL, M. G. 'The Teaching of Operational Research', *Operational Research Quarterly*, Vol. 9, No. 4 (December 1958)

A detailed discussion of how to introduce O.R. into a firm is given in RIVETT, P. and ACKOFF, R. *A Manager's Guide to Operational Research.* Wiley (1963)

PART IV: THE USE OF
OPERATIONAL RESEARCH

But what good came of it at last? Quoth little Peterkin.

ROBERT SOUTHEY: *After Blenheim*

Before 1950 most of the O.R. carried out was of a military nature. A good description of this will be found in *Science at War*, published by Penguin Books in 1947. The techniques used in this kind of O.R. in Britain and the U.S.A. are discussed by Morse and Kimball. Since 1950 O.R. has spread very rapidly into the industrial field and is now used extensively in the following industries: Oil, paper, chemical, metallurgical, general engineering, transport and distribution, mining and textiles. It is also used in civil government departments and in hospitals. There is no situation where a human or combined human and machine system exists for getting work done in which O.R. cannot be used to assess the efficiency of the programming aspect of the work.

The principal applications in the oil industry are the use of linear programming and its many ramifications to optimize refinery operations and solve distribution problems. These applications are described by Deam, Caplin, and Garvin in the papers referenced at the end of Part II.

Applications in the paper industry include the use of linear programming to minimize paper waste by choosing the optimum way of arranging the widths required by customers within the width of paper produced from the mill. Inspection techniques have been investigated because most inspection is visual and many problems of human error arise. Stock control problems have been studied, particularly by the firms which buy paper from the mills, for re-sale to the public in the form of note-paper or printing paper.

The applications of O.R. in the chemical industry include the following:

(1) The scheduling of the production of a variety of products through a multipurpose plant. Battersby (see Part II) studied this problem and used a computer programme to work out the schedule, taking into account the stock levels and rate of manufacture and sale for each product being made.

(2) The planning of production of a product having a seasonal selling pattern so that a uniform work load could be achieved with a minimum amount of capital tied up in stock. Agricultural chemicals are a typical illustration. The method of packaging and subsequent distribution to customers also needed to be taken into account.

(3) The chemical industry manufactures a number of intermediates that are used as the starting materials of a range of products. Operational Research is being used to study the problem of purchasing or manufacturing the intermediates and to determine the stocks required, bearing in mind customer service and the availability of certain intermediates.

(4) In some instances expensive batch reaction vessels are used and the failure of these can cause delays to customers unless a replacement vessel is available. A calculation of the failure distribution, using Monte Carlo techniques, can lead directly to an excellent ordering system.

(5) The distribution of some of the products of the industry can be expensive and in many cases a product may be made at a number of different factories. The allocation and distribution of products is required that gives the least cost to the company.

(6) The preparation of an overall optimum plan taking into account the sales pattern and any possible variations in operating conditions. This is closely related to what has been called 'Industrial Dynamics' and includes planning the size of future expansion.

In the metallurgical industry linear programming has been applied to metal mixing problems, queueing theory to the programming of furnaces and rolling mills (Banbury), probability theory and simulation methods to the optimum use of fuels in a steelworks. One of the largest O.R. groups in the U.K. is attached to the United Steel Company, and this team has carried out many studies into production control and automatic control of steelworks operations using advanced simulation techniques and employing both analogue and digital techniques for the purpose. A study of the power requirements of a steelworks resulted in a substantial saving in annual cost.

In general engineering a very wide variety of O.R. problems has been tackled. Queueing theory has been used in solving the problems associated with the production and storage of parts for subsequent assembly into machines or components thereof. This class of problem is discussed in Magee's book, referenced in Part II. Queueing theory has also been used in deciding upon the optimum number of machines which can be minded or maintained by one operative or engineer (Benson), linear programming has been used to make the best use of scattered storage depots (Schaafsma). Simulation is widely employed for planning jobbing operations and deciding upon the best allocation of machinery (Baker).

The transport and distribution industries have used O.R. for many allocation and routing problems. The two principal airways in the U.K., B.E.A. and B.O.A.C. employ O.R. staff to tackle the following types of problem.

(1) The provisioning of spare engines, etc., at overseas stations.

(2) Assessment of fuel reserves.

(3) Statistical and economic criteria justifying life extension of engines and components.

(4) The economics of uplifting fuel by weight rather than by volume.

(5) The joint effects of load factors and wind components on regularity.

(6) The economics of using alternative cruising procedures.

(7) Spares provisioning for a multiple input of components into a common overhaul unit.

(8) The effect of operational irregularity on ground handling at overseas stations.

(9) The effect of operational activity and irregularity on transport requirements.
(10) A study of the economic size of passenger aircraft.
(11) A comparison between alternative aircraft and component overhaul systems.
(12) The provision of reserve dishes for passenger meals in aircraft.
(13) A study of the implications of using a standard weight for pieces of passenger baggage in lieu of individual weights.

In the textile industry the British Cotton Industry Research Association has carried out numerous O.R. studies which have been summarized in two papers by Tippett. Cost studies are very important in this industry and investigations such as discovering the optimum size of bobbin to use in ring spinning have been carried out. The factors in the latter problem are that cost of space and power increase with bobbin size, whereas the cost of labour decreases.

The mining industry in the U.K. is mainly represented by the National Coal Board which has a very large O.R. Group. This has been concerned with the use of linear programming (Williams), underground communication systems and scale factors in the management of coal mines (Revans) and other problems (Hicks and Houlden).

The use of O.R. in civil government and hospitals is nothing like as extensive as it should be, but some useful work has been done by the Road Research Laboratories into traffic problems (Wardrop) and out-patients waiting problems have been studied by Bailey. These studies have led to the adoption of appointment systems in many hospitals. Further work is now being carried out at several London hospitals on administrative functions in conjunction with Work Study staff. The Ministry of Health has recently selected a group of experienced statisticians and administrators to advise him on the application of O.R. in hospitals.

Recently, there have been encouraging signs that local government is now using operational research. The creation of the local government operational research unit is one such sign. This O.R. team has been studying problems in many fields all of direct value in improving the standards of service and efficiency with which civic affairs are carried out. Their work has touched on such subjects as the collection and disposal of refuse, of school transport arrangements, financial administration and other problems arising from the growth and change of our towns (Ward).

Operational Research work has been carried out on advertising and has been published by Benjamin.

Some typical examples of O.R. in the U.S.A. are as follows:

The application of mathematical methods to production and employment scheduling of a paint factory (Holt *et al.*) utilized two decision rules, one to determine the aggregate rate of production and the other to establish the size of the work force. Since management required that both manpower and production stay between certain minimum and maximum limits, the rules were so designed that the resulting schedules met this requirement given a forecast of future plant orders, available manpower, and current inventory. At the end of each month, actual orders, manpower and inventories were used as feedback information when developing new schedules for succeeding time periods.

One major study was in the transportation industry in the analysis of railroad classification yards (Crane). Here inbound trains were broken up and their cars sorted into outgoing trains for various destinations. The activity in the yard consisted of two queueing systems in series. Monte Carlo procedures were used to simulate train arrivals and processing times. The effectiveness of the yard operation was then improved by varying the values of the parameters to minimize car waiting time and average queue lengths.

Queueing theory was used to determine the optimum number of clerks to assign to factory tool cribs (Brigham). This optimum number of clerks was based upon management's goals to keep overhead costs as low as possible, while at the same time to maintain adequate service for shop mechanics. Similar successes have been achieved in determining the optimum number of toll booths at traffic bridges and tunnels, and the optimum number of cash-registers in super markets.

The shipping operations of a medium-size manufacturing firm with widely distributed plants were subjected to a study utilizing the transportation formulation of a linear programming model (Batchelor). Two types of costs were used; production costs and freight costs. The total costs of all shipments, of all products, from all plants, to all destinations were minimum for the optimum schedule of trucks.

The inventory policies of a large company in a national distribution system were examined to determine optimum inventory levels and possible scope for reduction of distribution costs (Malcolm). The company had several factories and over 50 field warehouses. The study dealt with inventory determination of these field warehouses. The method was based on the notion of minimum total cost of inventory operations which included the cost of inventory depletion or stock run-out as well as the re-supply and inventory carrying costs. A comparison was made of the minimum total cost system with other systems of inventory control, and a criterion for evaluation of inventory systems was developed.

One type of problem to which Game theory has a direct application is where individuals or firms are in pure opposition. In the markets in which the size of the demand is more or less fixed by government or by habits, the extra customers that one firm can attract must be at the expense of competing firms. Game theory has been used in deciding on the timing of an advertising campaign (Charnes and Cooper), when several companies are competing for the same market. The advertising problem is treated as a series of games being played in each period where management chooses among alternative advertising campaigns involving different integrated programmes utilizing media of radio, television, newspapers, magazines and billboards.

Probability theory has been applied to a study of the effects of promotional efforts on sales (Magee). The company studied was engaged in distributing coffee to a large number of retail grocery stores. The significant characteristic for determining the amount a dealer would buy was the expected number of cases he would order in a specified time. The distribution of sales demand and the probability density function were based on existing data and served as basis for company demand from dealers following special promotions at selected stores. A quantitative measure of the effect of promotional effort was then established.

The theory of the optimum distribution of effort, initially used during World War II for determining the best way to deploy aircraft to locate submarines, has an industrial application in the problem of planning sales effort. A business with a limited number of salesmen (Ackoff), was studied to determine how sales time could be allocated between dealers with large stores, which usually produce large orders when visited, and small stores with correspondingly smaller sales return. As the probable return per visit for each store was known, the optimum distribution of sales effort could be calculated to maximize sales.

In a study for a major domestic airline (McCloskey and Hanssman) the optimal utilization of stewardesses and allocation of trips to bases was accomplished by solution of the assignment form of a linear programming problem. The assignment of stewardesses was reduced to the problem of optimal assignment of flights to bases. Time away-from-home was the objective function to be minimized. The problem of assignment was transformed to a series of two-city flight systems, for each of which the minimum away-from-home time was determined. Significant reduction in this time resulted in some reduction in the number of required stewardesses.

Information theory has been applied in one of the initial investigations into the problem of information processing (Macy), which involved communication under conditions of uncertainty. This uncertainty was in regard to the accuracy of the transmission of the symbols making up the message and the meaning that symbols were intended to convey. The meaning to be conveyed by the person originating the information was converted to a set of symbols in the coding process, the symbols were transmitted over a physical communication line, and decoded into a meaning by the person receiving the message. The discrepancies between the meaning sent and meaning received were designated as semantic noise and the principles of information theory were applied to establish a measure of this noise.

In auditing the accounts of a large metropolitan department store with a heavy volume of credit sales, statistical sampling was used for the ageing of the accounts receivable (Trueblood and Cyert). Receivables ageing is the process of determining the frequency distribution of the dollars in the total accounts receivable according to the length of time the dollars have been owed by the customers. Since the number of accounts was very large, ageing was performed on a sample drawn from the total universe of accounts receivable. The frequency distribution of dollars grouped according to age then was estimated for the universe from statistically drawn samples.

This has been a very sketchy review of the uses of O.R. in Great Britain and U.S.A., but a more detailed review would have been somewhat catalogued and tedious both to write and to read. Further information about the applications of O.R. both in the U.K. and in most of the countries of the world can be found in the *Proceedings of the First, Second and Third International Conferences on Operational Research* (English Universities Press, 1958, 1961 and 1964). Enough has probably been said, however, to illustrate the very wide scope and extensive use of Operational Research techniques and methodology.

REFERENCES

MORSE, P. M. and KIMBALL, G. E. *Methods of Operations Research.* Wiley (1951)

BANBURY, J. and TAYLOR, R. J. 'A Study of Congestion in the Melting Shop of a Steelworks', *Operational Research Quarterly* (June 1958)

BENSON, F. and COX, D. R. 'The Productivity of Machines Requiring Attention at Random Intervals', *Journal of the Royal Statistical Society*, No. 13, p. 65 (1951)

SCHAAFSMA, A. H. 'Making the best use of Scattered Storage Deports', *Metalworking Production* (July 20, 1956)

BAKER, C. T. and DZIELSINSKI, B. P. 'Simulation of a Simplified Job Shop', *I.B.M. Research Report*, R.C.–96 (May 15, 1959)

TIPPETT, L. H. C. 'Operational Research in Textiles', *Operational Research Quarterly* (June 1950) and 'Work Sampling applied to Operational Research', *Research*, Vol. 9 (1956)

WILLIAMS, K. B. and HALEY, K. B. 'A Practical Application of Linear Programming in the Mining Industry', *Operational Research Quarterly* (June 1959)

REVANS, R. W. 'Scale Factors in the Management of Coal Mines', *Operational Research Quarterly* (September 1953)

HICKS, D. and HOULDEN, B. T. 'Operational Research in the British Coal Industry', *Second International Conference on Operational Research.* English Universities Press (1961)

WARDROP, J. G. 'The Traffic Capacity of Weaving Sections of Roundabouts', *First International Conference on Operational Research.* English Universities Press (1957)

BAILEY, N. T. J. *Journal of the Royal Statistical Society*, B, No. 14, p. 185 (1952)

BENJAMIN, B. and MAITLAND, J. 'Operational Research and Advertising', *Operational Research Quarterly* (September 1958)

BRIGHAM, G. 'On a Congestion Problem in an Aircraft Factory (Boeing Airplane Company)', *Journal of Operations Research Society of America*, Vol. 3, No. 4 (1955)

CRANE, R. R. 'Analysis of a Railroad Classification Yard', *Journal of Operations Research Society of America*, Vol. 3, No. 3 (1955)

CHARNES, A. and COOPER, W. W. 'An Example of Constrained Games in Industrial Economics', *Econometrica* (1954)

ACKOFF, R. 'Allocation of Sales Effort', *Proceedings of the Conference on Operations Research in Industry*. Case Institute of Technology (April 1955)

HOLT, C. C., MODIGLIANI, F., SIMON, H. A. 'A Linear Decision Rule for Production and Employment Scheduling', *Management Science*, Vol. 2, No. 1 (1955)

MALCOLM, D. G. 'A Minimum Total Cost Approach to the Control of Distribution Inventories', delivered Eighth Annual Conference of American Institute of Industrial Engineers (1957)

BATCHELOR, J. H. *Proceedings of the Second Symposium in Linear Programming*, Vol. I. Washington, D.C. (1955)

MCCLOSKEY, J. and HANSSMANN, F. 'An Analysis of Stewardess Requirements and Scheduling for a Major Domestic Airline', *Naval Research Logistics*

MACY, J. 'Semantic Noise in an Information Processing Group', *Management Science*, Vol. 1 (1955)

MAGEE, J. 'The Effect of Promotional Effort on Sales', *Journal of the Operations Research Society of America*, Vol 1, No. 2 (1953)

TRUEBLOOD, R. and CYERT, R. *Sampling Techniques in Accounting*. Prentice Hall (1957)

WARD, R. A. *Operational Research in Local Government*. George Allen & Unwin in collaboration with the Royal Institute of Public Administration (1964)

CONCLUSION

I know why the Dodo
Has gone from land and sea
He lived Suaviter in Modo
Not Fortiter in Re!

Punch

It is my hope that by this stage I will have succeeded in conveying something of the philosophy of O.R. and that by means of the examples of the techniques used some of the potentialities and capabilities of the discipline will have been appreciated by the reader. This section will attempt to summarize what has been said, draw certain conclusions from it and leave the reader with, possibly, some stimulating thoughts.

In the first place it must be emphasized that this monograph is not intended as a comprehensive review of O.R. Much bigger and better books have already been written. Those by Churchman, *et al.*, and McCloskey, *et al.*, respectively referenced in Part I, are books which must be read by anyone who intends to carry out serious O.R. himself.

Nor does the treatment of O.R. in this monograph claim to be exhaustive. The references quoted are but a minute fraction of the enormous volume of literature on O.R. which has appeared in the last ten years. The bibliographies given at the end of Part II on O.R. and queueing list between them nearly 4,000 items and probably another 2,000 have appeared in *Applied Statistics, Operational Research Quarterly, Operations Research, Management Science, Harvard Business Review* and many other publications which regularly print articles on O.R. since these bibliographies were published.

To keep up with the world literature in any scientific subject nowadays is very nearly an impossibility and is certainly a task beyond me. To all those fellow O.R. workers whose important papers I have completely ignored I therefore humbly apologize.

All this monograph has attempted to do, as its title suggests, is to serve as a guide to the subject. It is intended to be read by business men, executives, administrators and managers who, realizing that their problems are growing more complex, are being forced to consider more complex means of solving them. Although the book has concentrated on industry for its examples, this is merely because my experience, with but few exceptions, has lain wholly within industry and it is a little less brash to preach about what you think you know than about what you clearly do not know. The methods of O.R. and especially the way of thought embodied in them, are equally applicable to commerce, to public administration, to such institutions as hospitals, and of course to military work in which it all started. In short, wherever there is a programming function to be carried out, O.R. will be found valuable.

It is not necessary in this complicated world of ours for everyone faced with a problem to know how to solve it. No one expects a managing director to be able to put to rights a technical process which has gone wrong. But he should at least have some perception of how to set about solving the problem and putting the process to rights. A managing director with no knowledge of the concepts underlying the manufacturing techniques used in his factories is not likely to be a good managing director.

A worth-while administrator makes himself aware of the concepts being applied in his organization, be they concerned with techniques, personnel or programming, and sees that they are in accord with the best available knowledge. This is a most vital task for the top man to perform, firstly, because he will probably be one of the men in the organization most capable of high level conceptual thinking and, secondly, because he is in the best position to see that viable concepts do not languish unused in remote corners.

In this scientific age it is natural that many of the newer concepts will be scientific in origin and one of the best results of World War II has been a recognition by business men of the respectability and validity of scientific concepts. Before 1939 very little applied scientific research was carried out in industry and practically no fundamental research. Now a great deal of both is carried out for industrial managers who see their necessity in the physical field.

It is now time for business men and administrators to recognize the validity of scientific concepts in the administrative sphere. These are the concepts of O.R. which are basically the concepts of all scientific endeavour.

The first of these concepts is that we are living in a world which is not wholly indeterminate. Bertrand Russell has pointed out that stability of environment is a necessity of civilization. If we did not have reasonable assurance that we would not vanish down a hole or disappear into thin air in the next five minutes, then all thoughts of planning for the future or of behaving in a moral and rational manner would vanish also.

Thus we can expect to use our experience of the past to predict the future. The business man who denies this confesses himself incapable of making a decision, or at least a rational one. To make a decision you must have some expectation of its outcome. That is to say, quite simply, you predict the future.

It cannot be predicted precisely, of course. If it could be, by any single person, he would make a fortune. If we all knew the future exactly, we would be automata with no decisions to make. Life in this world is possible, and interesting, because we can neither predict the future exactly nor is it unpredictable.

Science recognizes this and by study of the past delineates laws which increase our accuracy of prediction of the future. We know when the next eclipse of the sun will take place; to the natives in Rider Haggard's *King Solomon's Mines* it was a miracle.

Operational Research employs this concept of predictability through study by observing sales rates, machine breakdowns, arrival of orders and so on and by using the methods of mathematical statistics evolves the rules by which the frequencies of various occurrences can be predicted. This enables a greater degree of control on the object of study to be exercised by the manager in question.

The second scientific concept which should be used in business is that of experimentation. Aristotelian thought still dominates too many business discussions. You may remember that Aristotle and his disciples spent many hours discussing how many teeth a horse had.

When one of the disciples, with commendable temerity, suggested going and having a look at a horse the pure philosophical attitude of the other Greeks was shocked and no recorded action was taken. This same kind of discussion takes place on almost every business problem that exists.

The excuse, and it is not an unreasonable one, is that experimentation in business is too expensive and bankruptcy is no compensation for knowledge. This is where the third concept of O.R., the model, comes in. The model, be it a mathematical one as in Linear Programming, Queueing Theory or Stock and Production Control, or a physical simulation as in Monte Carlo Methods or Operational Gaming is set up to represent the real situation and experiments are carried out on the model, painlessly and without risk. Once these experiments are concluded to the satisfaction of the executive concerned and, as emphasized frequently, he must always be the final arbiter and his function is not being usurped, the decisions can then be taken.

The fourth, and final, concept is that of control. It is not sufficient to take a decision, however brilliantly reached, and leave it at that. Business environment is always changing and a decision which was correct at one time may be grossly in error some time later. The validity of the decision must be continually checked against the situation by means of feed back mechanisms as discussed in Cybernetics. The able administrator arranges his organization such that minor decisions are adjusted by homeostatic procedures down the executive line and do not trouble him. He must make sure, however, that these procedures do not attempt to modify the major decisions without his knowledge.

These then are the concepts of O.R. which this book had attempted to define, explain and illustrate in a manner which the executive can appreciate sufficiently for him to know how they can be used.

Two further points need making. It is sometimes felt to be necessary to justify any new departure in management philosophy on purely financial grounds. 'How much did it save?' the doubting Thomas's may be saying at every illustrative example in this book.

This is a very arid and unrewarding means of judging any innovation in industry. Firstly, the question is usually impossible to answer because the cost of any single aspect of a firm's business depends for its evaluation upon arbitrary definitions. If five operators are saved on a process, what is the financial saving? Their wages? Their wages, plus National Insurance, sick pay, etc.? Is part of a supervisor saved? Are the five operators dismissed or used elsewhere? What are the other consequences of the change? Is plant maintenance increased? What happens to overheads?

Secondly, the question is static in time. A change which may appear to save money in one situation may cause drastic losses in another. Thus a manager does not regard financial savings at one point of time as the sole measure of the value of an innovation.

Thirdly, it puts people's backs up. To arrive at any figure at all for financial saving requires some investigation. The people in the department or process on which the work has been done become well aware of this investigation and it is intensely annoying. 'What are these people trying to prove?' they think. 'That we were mugs in the first place and were wasting the firm's money?' No one likes to have that accusation levelled at him. Particularly as it often is not true. People do the best with the resources they have, by and large, and if management solve a problem by deploying more resources they should avoid any suggestion that it was anyone's fault other than their own that it was not solved before.

Judgement by financial saving sometimes causes an O.R. Department to try to justify its own existence by ferreting out evidence of such savings itself. This is fatal. Operational Research success is often born to blush unseen. It has been well said that if an O.R. worker brags about his success in any department he never does any useful work in that department again.

Besides, it is invidious to try to pin credit on any individual person or group. Industry depends upon team work. Operational Research in particular depends upon team work. The manager of a department, or members of his staff may often contribute as much, if not more, to the success of a project than the O.R. team, and to try to attach credit solely to the O.R. team is to arouse justifiable resentment.

The way to judge the success of an O.R. investigation is by the amount of control the manager in question has over the situation which he did not have before. Control is what a manager needs. The business environment is always changing, as has been stressed before, and to survive the business must change too. This cannot be achieved efficiently without control. The manager must know in which way the situation is changing and how he can rapidly adjust to it. If this can be done in many cases by homeostatic procedures, without him necessarily having to intervene, so much the better.

In the linear programming example published by Wyatt (p. 111) a change in economic conditions was correctly and automatically taken care of in the computation without any manager having to intervene. As a result of the queueing investigation by Robinson (p. 111) the manager in charge of estimating knew exactiy what he needed to meet his requirements.

Every successful O.R. investigation results in greater control being achieved by management. This is appreciated and understood by those concerned. There is no need for unreliable studies of cost saving to be carried out.

Of course, the O.R. solution may cost money and then there is a problem as to whether the greater control is worth the extra cost. But that is an O.R. problem.

Then the time scale of an O.R. project must be appreciated. Most worth-while things in this life take time to achieve and O.R. is no exception. The value of a project against time might be depicted in Figure 39 below:

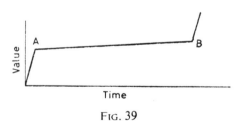

FIG. 39

Initially, there are usually some good results to report. Fresh minds on an old problem often shed valuable new light immediately. Then there is a long period while data is accumulated, contacts are established and thoughts are being communicated. This period may last from six months to several years. Then when point B is reached a conceptual break through occurs. Old routines can be scrapped and new ones instituted. A change in procedure which everyone finds

138

satisfying can be made and the manager finds himself in far more control of his situation than he was previously. This conceptual break through, when it occurs, is worth all the uncertainties of the period AB, when little progress seemed to be made. This is when O.R. is found to be really worth while.

Finally, may I close with a plea to those managers who have read this far and especially to any heads of organizations with substantial financial resources. Operational Research so far has been carried out largely on individual projects in individual firms. No great general principles of industrial programming have yet had a chance to emerge because no work in this field has been possible. Operational Research could give tremendous help to managers in discovering fundamental laws governing such things as permissible rates of growth of firms, acceptable profit ratios, desirable staff turnover rates and so on. I hope some wealthy, imaginative business man will promote and support such O.R. studies.

APPENDIX I: RAPID STATISTICAL TESTS FOR USE BY MANAGERS

The job of a manager is to make decisions: the job of O.R. is to help him. Most of the techniques of O.R. such as linear programming and queueing theory are too complicated to be mastered and applied by the manager himself without a good deal of study, the time for which he can rarely spare. Thus a lot of what has been said in this book about the value and efficiency of these methods must be taken on trust by the manager if he is to apply them.

There are, however, some simple techniques in mathematical statistics which can be used by any executive who is sufficiently interested to read this appendix carefully and to note in his diary or other conveniently referenced place the relevant test criteria. These tests can be used to assist in making decisions which involve the analysis of data. Where, for example, some output figures have been produced and where it is necessary to have some assessment as to the information these figures contain. By using these tests the manager can gain some appreciation of the kind of thinking used in O.R. work and get experience of the validity and usefulness of the O.R. approach.

The tests can be used to decide whether the average of a sample departs significantly from a known mean, whether two samples differ significantly from each other, whether one outstanding number in a group should be discarded or not, whether a group of consecutive numbers displays a trend or exhibits other non-random behaviour, or whether two consecutive samples are significantly correlated. The term significant is used in the statistical sense, i.e. an event is considered significant if its occurrence by chance is comparatively rare. In normal statistical usage an event which would only occur by chance once in twenty times is judged significant. This is a smaller probability than that of getting four heads with successive throws of a coin. You can assess for yourself whether this criterion is adequate to guard against random interference in judgement by taking a coin and tossing it four times. The frequency with which four heads appear on successive throws is somewhat greater than the frequency with which these statistical tests will give a misleading interpretation.

Significance of a mean

Here is one of the rapid tests.

Twenty-one scrap results give the following figures; in percentages

12·3, 11·5. 10·6, 8·7, 13·6, 7·8, 13·5, 12·0, 11·1, 10·7, 11·3, 9·5, 12·9, 11·1, 10·3, 12·6, 9·8, 10·6, 9·2, 10·8, 10·9

The previous average scrap level was 10·3 per cent. Has the incidence of scrap changed or not?

There is no need to work out the new average, a tedious business. You merely count how many figures are higher than 10·3 and how many are lower, ignoring any which are equal to 10·3. There are 15 numbers higher than 10·3 and 5 lower. The difference between 15 and 5 is $15-5 = 10$. The sum of 15 and 5 is $15+5 = 20$. The rule for significance (at the one-in-twenty level) is that 'difference' must be greater than twice square-root sum.

In this case difference = 10.
Square-root sum = square root of 20, which is $4\frac{1}{2}$ (approx.)
Twice square-root sum = 9 (approx.)

Therefore difference is greater than twice square-root sum and there has been a significant shift in the scrap level.

Try another example.

Is the average of the following 16 numbers significantly different from 24:

27, 22, 19, 23, 20, 28, 21, 30, 18, 24, 16, 26, 23, 20, 23, 21.

There are 4 numbers more than 24; 11 less than 24.

Difference is $11-4 = 7$
Sum is $11+4 = 15$
Twice square-root sum = $2\sqrt{15}$ = twice 4 (approx.) = 8(approx.)

Difference is therefore less than square-root sum and hence the average is not significantly different from 24.

The average *is* different of course and what this statement really means is that the average of the population of which these numbers are a sample may not be different from 24. In life you always examine a sample – a year's production figures are just a sample of the possible population of years' production figures and what you are trying to determine from the sample is the properties of the population. What, in other words, the 'true' average would be if you knew it. Here you have no sound evidence that the 'true' average is different from 24, and to act as if it were may be unwise.

You may have to act, of course, and you may be so perturbed about the difference that you might well act as if it were significantly different, and you may well be right. The statistical test does not tell you what to do, obviously, but it tells you how justified you are *on the data alone* in taking what action you do. In this case on the data alone you are not justified in acting as if the 'true' average of the group was different from 24, but you may have other considerations to take into account. You may be in a situation where there is no harm done if you assume the average is different and you are wrong, whereas harm would be done if you assumed the average were not different and you were wrong. In that situation clearly you would act as if the average were different, but if there were no compelling reason for acting one way in preference to another then it would be better to collect more data.

There is a simple rule about the extra amount of data to collect. In the second example, above the 'difference' count was 7 and this was not significant because it was less than $2\sqrt{15}$, where 15 was the 'sum' count. If, however, the 'true' average of the group of numbers examined were less that 24, and the only reason this has not been clear so far is because there was inadequate data, then the amount of data we need to make certain is

$$\left(\frac{\text{twice sum}}{\text{difference}}\right)^2$$

In this example it would be

$$\left(\frac{2 \times 15}{7}\right)^2 = 18$$

Three more observations would therefore be required *provided* that the 'true' average of the group was below 24.

Clearly, if three more observations were taken and at least one were greater than 24, then a repeat test would still not show a significant difference for:

New sum $= 18$
New difference $= 13 - 5 = 8$
Twice square-root sum $= 2\sqrt{18} = 8\frac{1}{2}$

which is still greater than the difference.

A repeat test is thus necessary after the further data has been collected, and this may indicate that still further information is needed. The amount of this can be calculated.

If only a small amount of extra data is needed, then this may be readily collected, and the manager may well be prepared to take what he feels to be the appropriate decision while it is being collected. If a large amount of extra data is needed, which would certainly be the case if the initial test gave a result which was far from being significant, then this may serve to emphasize to the manager the inadequate basis for any decision which would imply significance in the data.

Significance of the difference between two means

This same rapid test can be used to determine whether two groups of numbers differ significantly from one another.

Take the weekly outputs of two factories, as shown below:

Week	Factory A	Factory B	Difference A − B
1	1,700	1,600	+
2	2,900	3,300	−
3	1,700	2,000	−
4	2,500	2,800	−
5	2,800	3,500	−
6	1,100	2,000	−
7	2,500	3,200	−
8	2,100	3,700	−
9	1,200	2,900	−

It is merely necessary to take the sign of the difference between the

A and B figures and to compare the number of plus signs with the number of minus signs:

Number of plus signs = 1
Number of minus signs = 8
Difference is $8 - 1 = 7$
Sum is $8 + 1 = 9$
Twice square-root sum = $2\sqrt{9}$ = twice 3 = 6

Difference is more than twice square-root sum, so the output of Factory A is significantly lower than that of Factory B.

If the difference had not been significant but there was sufficient difference to make us suspect that more information would have revealed a difference, then the total number of weeks output required to establish significance for this difference if it persisted is again

$$\left(\frac{\text{twice sum}}{\text{difference}}\right)^2$$

Test for a trend

It is often important to know when figures are showing a trend up or down. Scrap may appear to be increasing, output may appear to be falling. Before taking action the executive may want to satisfy himself that the trend is real and is not due to chance.

The figures can be examined in the following way. Divide them into three equal, or approximately equal portions, and compare the third portion with the first one.

Example

The following figures appear to show a trend:

9·5, 9·1, 9·0, 9·5, 10·0, 10·0, 10·2, 10·7, 10·4, 11·5, 11·2, 11·6, 10·2, 11·8, 12·0

There are fifteen numbers. Divided into three equal groups of five numbers they become:

  (i)   9·5   9·1   9·0   9·5 10·0
  (ii) 10·0 10·2 10·7 10·4 11·5
  (iii) 11·2 11·6 10·2 11·8 12·0

Comparing the first group with the third it is seen that each number in the third group is higher than its equivalent one in the first group.

11·2 is higher than 9·5, 11·6 is higher than 9·1 and so on. There are five comparisons and in each one the third group is higher. To decide whether this means that the third group is significantly greater than the first group use the same formula $2\sqrt{N}$ described earlier. In this case N is the total number of comparisons between the two groups and $2\sqrt{N}$ is the amount by which the comparisons favourable to the third group must exceed those favourable to the first group. In the above example $N = 5$, therefore $2\sqrt{N} = 4\cdot5$.

The number of comparisons favourable to the third group was 5, the number favourable to the first group was zero.

The difference was therefore 5, which is greater than 4·5 and hence the observed trend is significant.

Example

Is there a trend in the following figures?

20, 21, 37, 25, 39, 46, 29, 10, 49, 45, 15, 7, 57, 44, 23, 28, 59, 50, 40, 31, 41, 24, 47, 51, 42, 47, 55, 47

There are 28 numbers, so the first and third groups contain 9 each in which the comparisons are as follows:

Comparison	Favourable to first group	Favourable to third group
20, 31	–	1
21, 41	–	1
37, 24	1	–
25, 47	–	1
39, 51	–	1
46, 42	1	–
29, 47	–	1
10, 55	–	1
49, 47	1	–
	3	6

The excess number is 3,

$$N = 9$$
$$2\sqrt{N} = 2\sqrt{9} = 6$$

3 is less than 6 so there is no evidence of the existence of a trend. Further information could of course be collected. The amount of further information necessary is given by the same formula

$$\left(\frac{\text{twice sum}}{\text{difference}}\right)^2$$

as before.

Association

It is very often necessary to know whether two groups of numbers are connected, whether, for example, scrap increases as output falls, or whether the   st of consumable supplies is related to output. A rapid test for an association of this nature between numbers is illustrated below:

A	B
4·9	8·6
5·3	8·7
4·7	8·5
5·1	8·6
5·4	8·6
4·6	8·4
5·0	8·5
5·5	8·7
4·8	8·5
4·5	8·5
5·2	8·6
Average 5·0	Average 8·55

The number of pairs in which *both* figures are higher and both figures are lower than the respective average is then counted. In this example there are nine such pairs, i.e. all pairs except.

$$4·9 \qquad 8·6$$
$$\text{and}$$
$$5·0 \qquad 8·5$$

The number of pairs in which one figure is higher and the other figure lower than the respective average is then counted. In this case it is one

$$4 \cdot 9 \qquad 8 \cdot 6$$

The pair 5·0 and 8·5 is not included because 5·0 is the average of one group.

The difference between the two sets of pairs is then calculated and this is once more assessed by the $2\sqrt{N}$ criterion.

In this example the difference is $9 - 1 = 8$
The total number of pairs, N, is 10
Therefore $2 \sqrt{N} = 2 \times 3 \cdot 3 = 6 \cdot 6$

8 is greater than 6·6, therefore the association is significant.

Example

Is there an association between the following pairs of numbers?

14·7	2·80
13·4	2·74
14·9	2·73
14·7	2·81
13·2	2·78
13·0	2·70
14·3	2·69
15·0	2·83
13·4	2·72
13·7	2·80
13·3	2·73
14·7	2·77
Average 14·0	Average 2·76

The numbers of pairs in which *both* figures are higher or lower than the respective average is 8. The numbers of pairs in which one figure is higher and the other lower is 4.

The difference is thus $8 - 4 = 4$
The total number of pairs is 12

$$2\sqrt{12} = 7$$

4 is less than 7, so there is no significant association.

Once again the amount of further information necessary to establish a significant association, if such exists, can be predicted from the formula given.

Spotting a stranger

Sometimes when a group of numbers is examined one or two figures do not seem to belong. An example is given below.

1·04, 6·75, 7·97, 9·72, 3·51, 2·62, 26·54, 3·66, 8·09

In this group the number 26·54 seems to be a stranger. How can we be sure it is all right to reject it from the group or to make it the subject of a special enquiry?

The test is to subtract the smallest observation in the group from the largest, first including the suspected stranger and then excluding the suspected stranger. In this case we get:

$$26·54 - 1·04 = 25·50$$

and $$9·72 - 1·04 = 8·68$$

The ratio of these ranges is about 3.

If the range with the suspected stranger is at least twice the range without the suspected stranger, then the suspected stranger does not belong to the group. The statistical test does not of itself however provide sufficient justification for rejecting the suspect figure. Some physical reason such as abnormal conditions under which the particular figure was obtained must be discovered before analysis of the data can safely proceed.

Example

10·3, 11·5, 3·1, 13·7, 14·3, 13·8, 11·9
Is 3·1 a stranger?

The range including 3·1 is $14·3 - 3·1 = 11·2$
The range excluding 3·1 is $14·3 - 10·3 = 4·0$

Thus $\dfrac{11·2}{4·0} = 2·8$

This is more than 2, hence 3·1 is a stranger.

REFERENCES

Further information on quick statistical tests can be obtained from the following sources:

DUCKWORTH, W. E. and WYATT, J. K. 'Rapid Statistical Techniques for Operational Research Workers', *Operational Research Quarterly*, Vol. 9, No 3, p. 218 (September 1958)

MOORE, P. B. 'Some Approximate Statistical Tests', *Operational Research Quarterly*, Vol. 10, No. 1, p. 41 (March 1959)

QUENOUILLE, M. H. *Rapid Statistical Calculations*. Griffin (1959)

APPENDIX II: BUSINESS MODELS PROJECT RULES OF PLAY

Background

Three Motor Companies, Alpha, Beta and Gamma have decided to manufacture a new, and revolutionary, type of small car. For this purpose they are each setting up a small company with an initial maximum output of 200 vehicles per annum. This small initial output is justified by the novelty of this type of vehicle and the fact that the British motoring public is very conservative in its reaction to this kind of innovation. Capacity can be expanded fairly rapidly should the need arise.

The vehicle was developed at the Delta Research Association and although patent rights are exclusive to Britain free licences will be granted to any British firm. At present only Alpha, Beta and Gamma are interested enough to start manufacture but other companies may follow suit if the market shows signs of rapid expansion. For this reason, and because motor car sales are traditionally somewhat volatile and subject to rapid Government pressure by means of purchase tax and hire-purchase changes, the future sales of the vehicle are uncertain.

Each company is being set up as an independent concern and you, as its board of directors, are in sole charge. It must stand on its own feet and no borrowing or subsidies from the parent company are permitted. A plant has been built capable of making 50 vehicles per quarter, 50 vehicles have already been manufactured and 50 are in progress when you take over. (All these details will be summarized later for convenient reference.) Five salesmen from the parent company have been assigned to you and all the staff necessary to run the factory has been recruited. As well as these assets the initial working capital of the company is £100,000 cash.

The vehicles are to be sold in units of two through general distributors who are not tied to any company. These have been chosen to cover most of Great Britain and there are 9 in urban districts and 15 in rural areas, making 24 in all. These are split into four regions. Selling these cars is a very skilled job requiring a lot of technical knowledge and a great deal of customer liaison work. Because of this a salesman can only deal with up to two customers in adjacent urban areas in any quarter and only one customer in any rural district. Only one salesman should deal with one customer in any one quarter. Further salesmen cost £4,000 to hire and train and it is a year before they can operate on their own. During the training period they make no contribution to sales effort. You can pay your salesmen what you wish. The five you have initially are being paid £2,000 a year because the level of the job justifies this. These highly skilled salesmen are greatly in demand by other firms and you must expect a turnover of around 20 per cent per annum at the above salary. You can reduce this turnover by paying a higher salary or increase it by paying less. Should you have to reduce salaries at any stage an immediate loss of several salemen is likely, but not certain. All salesmen must be paid the same salary, and salary reviews are twice yearly. This does not mean that salaries need be increased at those times, they cannot be increased oftener than twice a year.

You can sell your vehicles to the distributors at any price you please. The initial price agreed on between the parent companies and the distributors is £400 each. Your sales will vary with price, price variations are permitted only every six months, all vehicles in any quarter must be sold at the same price. Your price is not advertised, you and your competitors can only discover each other's prices in any quarter at a cost of £500 for each competitor.

You can sell from Work in Progress (W.I.P.) but goodwill is lost. If you effect a sale and cannot supply, goodwill is also lost.

You can increase your sales by advertising. A page of advertising in any one region per quarter costs £1,250 and you can have up to five pages of advertising per region per quarter. Persistent advertising by all companies will have the effect of raising sales potential in the affected regions.

You can also increase your sales by improving the product. This requires further research which you cannot afford to do yourself but

Fig. 40 BUSINESS MODELS PROJECT

Company _____ Quarter _____ Year _____

DISPOSITION OF CASH

EXPENDITURE IN QUARTER	£		CASH RESOURCES	£
Salaries . . .			Beginning Cash . .	100,000
Hiring . . .				
Advertising . .			A/R Collection . .	
R. & D. . . .				
Staff Work . .			A/R Factored . .	
Factoring . . .			Loan . . .	
TOTAL EXPENSES			**TOTAL INCOME** .	100,000
Plant Investment .				
Loan Repayment .				
Work in Process				
(Sched. last qtr.) .				
Fixed Cost .	£3,000			
Variable Cost (50)	£5,000		**TOTAL OUTGO** .	
Total	£8,000			
TOTAL OUTGO .			**ENDING CASH BALANCE** .	

SALES VISITS
Indicate visit
by ticks, so:

[✓]

SALES

1 [ ]
2 [ ]
3 [ ]
4 [ ]
5 [ ]
6 [ ]
7 [ ]
8 [ ]
9 [ ]
10 [ ]

Price

PRODUCTION COSTING

			Avg. Cost
beginning of quarter			£160
Production last Quarter	50	8,000	
Total Stock	50	8,000	
Units Sold (at avg. Cost)			
Closing Inventory			

SUMMARY OF ASSETS

£

Ending Cash Balance . . _____
Accounts Receivable . . _____

Inventory . . _____
Work in Progress . . _____
Plant . . _____
(*Less* Loan Outstanding) . . _____
Total Assets . . _____
Change in Total Assets (Assets last Quarter) . | £108,000 |

Salesmen's Salaries

Personnel Analysis
No. in Field ___ 5
No. Resigned ___

QUARTER'S PROFIT AND LOSS ACCOUNT

£

Sales Receipts . . _____
Total Production Cost . . _____
Gross Profit . _____
Total Expenses . . _____
Net Profit . . _____

12 ☐
13 ☐
14 ☐
15 ☐
16 ☐
17 ☐
18 ☐
19 ☐
20 ☐
21 ☐
22 ☐
23 ☐
24 ☐

TOTAL SALES _____

which the parent company will do for you on a fee-paying basis. The minimum fee is £4,000 per quarter and this can be raised in steps of £4,000. The success of the research depends upon the cumulative sum spent on it and this need not have been a continuous expenditure. If you do not spend anything on research for a period it will not adversely affect your chance of a product improvement once you have spent the required sum.

Your initial fixed production costs are £3,000 per quarter and the variable costs per vehicle are £100. Production can vary from 20 to 50 cars in steps of 10. You can increase your capacity in steps of 50 vehicles by spending £12,000 on new plant. You must never produce below 40 per cent of your capacity however and all production must be in units of 10. The fixed and variable costs of operating with increased capacity will be made known to you, at the time the increased capacity comes into operation, or in advance at a cost of £1,000. Extra plant takes nine months to build, but you can schedule extra vehicles after three months.

You can discover information about your competitors and the market by carrying out appropriate investigations. The costs of these are given in the schedule provided. Every year a balance sheet of each company will be published.

You sell on credit, payment to be made in six months. If you borrow on accounts receivable the cost is 10 per cent of the amount borrowed, i.e. 'factored'.

One of the important features of the model is the accurate keeping of accounts on the appropriate form. To induce a proper feeling of responsibility in the use of this form no sales will be permitted to a company that makes a mistake, in the quarter in which the mistake is *detected*.

Cycle of operations

You will begin with a game board laid out as follows:

    5 salesmen in the 'Field' position
    1 plant in the 'On Stream' position
    5 units representing 50 cars in the 'Inventory' position
    5 units representing 50 cars in the 'W.I.P.' position

The decision form will be filled in with

Beginning Cash	£100,000
Total Assets	£108,000

Work in process

Fixed Cost	£3,000
Variable Cost (5)	£5,000
Total	£8,000

Personnel analysis

No. in Field: 5

Production costing	*Units*	£
Inventory at beginning of Quarter .	–	–
Production last Quarter . .	50	8,000
Total Stock. . . .	50	8,000
Average cost. £160		

The action you will then take is as follows:

1. You will decide what salary to pay your salesmen. This will be fixed for six months.
2. You will decide whether to hire any more salesmen at a cost of £4,000 each.
3. You will decide how much to spend on advertising and in what region, at a cost of £1,250 per page per region with a maximum of five pages per region per quarter.
4. You will decide what to spend on R. & D., in £4,000 steps.
5. You will decide what to spend on staff work, according to the schedule of costs provided.
6. You will decide what to spend on extra plant, at £12,000 per plant.
7. The loan repayment section should be ignored, loans may be made available at a later stage of the game if found necessary, but this is unlikely.
8. You will then total your outgo and it must not be greater than your total income, initially £100,000. The ending cash balance should be inserted in the two places provided.

9. You will decide your price and insert in the appropriate box. This is fixed for six months.
10. You will decide on what amount to schedule for next time, in units from 20 to 50.
11. You will decide upon the distribution of your five salesmen among customers, noting that one salesman can visit two of customers 1–6 and 22–24 providing they are on adjacent squares of the game board, but only one of the remaining customers. You will note the distribution of salesmen in the squares on the left-hand side of the form. Only one tick should be in any square.
12. For this sequence of 11 stages you will be allowed 20 minutes. At the end of that time the umpire attached to your team, who may or may not be present during this period, will collect the form from you. If there are any mistakes there will be no sales.
13. The umpire will
    (a) calculate the sales, insert the total quantity sold and where the sales have occurred;
    (b) calculate the results of research expenditure and inform all teams of any product improvements;
    (c) give all the teams the results of any staff work;
    (d) calculate number of salesmen resigning;
    (e) insert fixed and variables costs of new W.I.P. on new form;
    (f) return old form and new form to team.
14. You will then have 20 minutes in which to do the following:
15. Move relevant counters one place up on game board.
16. Insert units sold and cost in the Production Costing section and calculate closing inventory.
17. Insert sales receipts, etc., in Quarter's Profit and Loss Account and calculate net profit.
18. Complete Summary of Assets. The Change in Total Assets must equal net profit.
19. Resume cycle (1) to (11). Note that decisions (1) and (9) are not applicable if a change was made in the previous quarter.

Each 'year' when the annual Balance Sheets are published the decision period permitted will be 30 minutes, to allow time for digestion of these.